Elke Haltia

W9-CQB-101

Beyond a
Broken
Promise

CAMPUS LIFE BOOKS

Beyond a Broken Promise

GREGG LEWIS

A DIVISION OF CTi
CampusLife
BOOKS

LIVING
BOOKS ®

Living Books is a registered trademark of Tyndale
House Publishers, Inc.

First printing, December 1988

Library of Congress Catalog Card·Number 88-51241
ISBN 0-8423-0344-8
Copyright 1988 by Campus Life Books, a division of CTi
Printed in the United States of America

INTRODUCTION

I sat in the lobby of a college dormitory one evening and listened as a nineteen-year-old girl, with tears running down her face, recounted the day her father told her he was leaving. She knew for two hours before her mother did; her father hoped she'd be able to help her mother accept the news. "It's been almost three years," she said, "but just telling you about it brings back all the feelings."

A twenty-year-old guy admitted, "I have to pray every day that God will help me not to hate my father for what he did to our family."

A college freshman told me the only time he hears from his father is at Christmas and on his birthday. "He shows up with an armload of presents," he said, his voice cracking with emotion. "And I feel like screaming, 'I don't want any presents; I want a father!'"

"I know love is supposed to bind people together, and I love both my parents very much," one sixteen-year-old girl told me. "But when your parents divorce, the love you have just rips you in two."

"I think divorce is worse than having a parent die. At least after a funeral the death itself is past," said a college sophomore. "A divorce never ends. The pain just keeps going on."

Every teenager and young adult I talked to relived his or her own hurts. But time after time, when I thanked them for so willingly sharing their difficult experiences, they replied, "If I can do anything to help one other person who's going through what I went through, I'm glad to do it."

I sat for three hours one night with a group of six high school students who talked about their feelings concerning their parents' divorces, the struggles of living in a one-parent family, the effect their parents' experiences had on their own attitudes toward relationships and marriage, and a lot of other related topics. At the end of the time I asked them who they talked to about these subjects. Everyone of them said they'd never had a discussion like that before. They'd never talked to anyone—not parents, not friends, not teachers, not pastors—about their deepest feelings or the problems they'd faced or the impact divorce had had in their own lives. But they all agreed that it had been such a positive, helpful experience to share with and listen to others who understood what they'd gone through, that they were willing to meet again right away.

When I asked people I interviewed what they'd read about divorce as they tried to deal with their own situation, I was surprised to hear most of them say, "Nothing." So I became convinced that *Campus Life* needed to do a book on this subject.

I started out thinking this book would tell one person's true story. But I heard so many poignant stories from so many people that I decided not to do that. Instead I sifted and combined the stories into one.

Some of the details you are about to read have been changed and identities have been disguised. But the emotions—and the pain—are real. Many of the words are the words I heard from the young people who talked to me.

So the book you are about to read is not just one person's true story. It's a lot of people's story. And in that sense, it's all too true.

If you're a young person whose family has come apart, you may see and feel some of your own pain in this book. If so, I pray it'll help you better understand and cope with your own experience.

If you have a friend from a divorced home, you may see some of his or her feelings and experiences in this book. If so, I pray it'll help you be more sensitive to your friend's struggles and needs.

If you're a parent or you work with young people, you may see some young person you know in the following pages. If so, I pray it will give you insight and understanding that will enrich your relationships.

Gregg Lewis

CHAPTER

1

If I were a pessimist, maybe I would have expected something terrible to happen because everything was going so good. But I'm not. So I never saw it coming. Until it hit me like a truck.

Looking back, I'd say the story started, at least from my perspective, the night Jennifer Heinz and I had our first real date. I'd only known her for a couple of months. It'd been that long since she'd started coming to the youth group at my church. I'd noticed her right away. All the guys did. Any girl who stands 5'10" with flaming red hair hanging halfway down her back would be pretty hard to miss in any crowd, let alone our little group of twenty-five members. She was thin, but with a nice figure which I have to admit I noticed. Her eyes were sorta between blue and green, depending on the light. And a smattering of freckles spread across the bridge of her nose and under her eyes.

She went to a high school in another nearby suburb, which meant I had to ask around to learn that she did date some. But no one regular. So I made it a point to talk to her the second week. A couple of weeks later I sat beside her during our meeting.

There was something intriguing about her, besides her looks. She seemed friendly enough; she smiled easily. She was a little shy and guarded maybe. Yet underneath there was a vulnerability that helped me work up the courage to finally ask her out.

"You got a ride home tonight?" I asked her during refreshments one Sunday night.

She shook her head. "I'm supposed to call my mom when the meeting's over if I need a ride."

"I've got my dad's car tonight. I can take you if it's all right."

"It's not exactly on your way home. I live about twenty minutes from here."

"It's OK with me if it's OK with you."

She smiled. "Sure."

So far, so good, I thought as we walked to the car.

Twenty minutes never seemed so short. We made casual small talk about plans for summer vacation and about school. She interrupted occasionally to give directions to her house. And suddenly we were there.

As I pulled into the driveway and coasted to a stop, she reached for the door handle. "Thanks for the ride, Matt. I'll see you next week."

"No problem," I said. Her door opened and she swung her legs out. *It's now or never.* "I was, uh, wondering. Would you like to go out Friday night? Maybe play some miniature golf and then grab a hamburger or something to eat?"

"I'm not so hot at golf," she said.

"If you'd rather do something else . . ."

"No," she said, smiling again. "I just thought I should warn you. It sounds like fun. What time?"

"Oh, it's about 8:47."

"What time Fri—," then she saw my grin and laughed. It was a very nice sound.

"Pick you up at seven?" I asked.

"Fine," she smiled. "See you then." If I hadn't had to drive Dad's car, I might have flown home.

I thought a lot about Jennifer that week. I almost called her to ask if she would rather do something besides miniature golf. But I talked myself out of that. I knew it was silly to be so uptight about a date. It wasn't as if I'd never been out with a girl before. I'd dated four. One for six months during the tenth grade.

At 6'2" and 163 pounds, I wasn't exactly what my twelve-year-old sister would call a "hunk." My mom called me scrawny. I preferred the term "lanky." And while I didn't expect Hollywood to ever make my face famous, I'd always been fairly satisfied with my ordinary brown eyes and short brown hair, and my slightly distinguished Roman nose.

So I felt a little funny standing in front of the bathroom mirror at 6:35 Friday evening, surveying my red knit short-sleeved shirt and my white shorts and suddenly wondering if my nose would look less prominent if I parted my hair down the middle instead of on the left. "Get going, Guthrie," I finally told myself, taking a swig of Scope and spitting into the sink. "It's just a date."

Even so, I spent the entire drive to Jennifer's in renewed debate with myself over whether or not to suggest an alternative to miniature golf. I considered going to a movie. You can sit for two hours in a dark theater and not have to worry about conversation. But I really did want to get to know Jennifer better. Miniature golf would give us something to do while we talked and that was always easier. By the time I pulled into Jennifer's driveway I'd decided for the fourth and final time to stick with the original plan.

But the moment Jennifer met me at the door it no longer mattered. I'd have been happy to go anywhere with her. She was wearing green shorts and a matching green top that made her red hair look richer than I'd remembered. I tried not to gawk and covered the sudden pounding of my heart by asking the obvious: "Are you ready?"

"As long as you remember my warning. I'm really not any good at golf."

She was right. I parred the first three holes. She was eight over par.

"Do you have any suggestions?" she asked as she teed up for the fourth hole.

"Yeah. You're holding the putter a little too much like a baseball bat. Try moving your left thumb. . . . Here let me show you." I leaned my own putter against a fence and helped her adjust her grip. Her hands felt warm, and just touching them sent a tingling shiver through me. "And when you hit the ball, don't just tap it, try to stroke through it."

"Like this?" She hit her ball and it rolled down the carpet, bounced around a dogleg and climbed up onto a little elevated green to stop less than a foot from the hole.

I putted, but my shot missed the angle on the dogleg and rolled back toward me instead of around toward the green. I putted again and the ball went around the corner and up the slope to stop two feet from the hole.

I putted out with a three before Jennifer lined up her second shot. It dropped for a two and she laughed in delight. "Would you like me to give you a little advice on this next hole?"

"Hey, don't get too cocky," I said, faking a frown. "That was just beginner's luck." But I hoped it wasn't. In fact, I'd have gladly lost every hole just to hear her laugh. I didn't. But Jennifer did improve dramatically by the time we finished our second round and quit to go get something to eat.

We stopped at a little drive-in hamburger stand called McDougal's, which capitalizes on its slightly different name and the fact that it offers old-time curb service to provide a surprising amount of competition to the big-name franchises in town. I pushed the little red button on the speaker outside my window and placed our order. I wanted a "Big Dougal" with everything and a large chocolate malt. Jennifer asked for a cheeseburger and a medium 7-Up and we agreed to split a large order of fries.

While we waited for our food, I asked her about her family. She said she had a sister, Joan, who was twenty and in college. Her nineteen-year-old brother, Phil, worked. And her little sister, Valerie, was twelve. She and Valerie were the only ones living at home. They lived with their mom, since her parents had been divorced for more than six years.

The carhop showed up with our food about then and as we were about to eat, Jennifer asked about my family.

I remember exactly what I said: "We're your regular, normal American family with three kids and a dog." I winced inside as soon as I said it because I didn't mean to imply her family wasn't normal; it was just the way

I'd always thought about my family. Jennifer didn't seem to take any offense so I hurried on to cover my insensitivity. "I'm the oldest. I've got a a twelve-year-old sister, too, named Melissa. And a little brother, Mark, who's in kindergarten and just turned six. You've probably seen my parents at church. Dad's a district sales manager for a company that makes outdoor camping equipment and my mom keeps busy being a mom and volunteering a couple of days a week as a teacher's aide at the day care center at the church."

I stopped and took the first bite of my Big Dougal as Jennifer said, "I've often wished I'd been the oldest in my family. It seems like there are so many advantages."

"I don't know. I suppose there are some advantages, some privileges. But there's a down side, too."

"Like what?" she asked between bites.

"You have extra responsibilities. Your parents expect more out of you. And sometimes I think you're sort of a guinea pig for your parents to practice on so they can do a better job with the younger siblings. In fact," I grinned, "I think younger children the world over owe a great debt of gratitude to their elders for doing most of the work in breaking in parents."

Jennifer laughed, and we talked about that for a while. She made me give examples to back up my opinion, and she countered some of them with examples of her own as a middle kid.

She finally changed the subject by asking: "Tell me about your parents—are you more like your mom or your dad?"

That stumped me for a minute. I'd never really thought about that before, at least not to try to explain it. "That's a tough one. I've always considered my parents as very different people."

"In what ways?"

"My dad's a real go-getter. I guess that's the kind of personality it takes to be a successful salesman. He's never reluctant to walk into a new situation. He likes to push himself. He relishes adventure and new experiences. One of his favorite mottoes is 'Never turn down a new experience as long as it's morally acceptable.' He told me that when he was a college student he heard a speaker say that was good advice for anyone wanting to be a creative, interesting, and growing person. He's made it sort of a family motto as well."

"What about your mom?" Jennifer had finished her hamburger and had tucked one of her long legs under her on the bucket seat. She was turned toward me, leaning back comfortably against the passenger door, ready to listen.

"In some ways, she's just the opposite. She's kind of quiet in a group of people. I think she actually enjoys a regular routine. She worries a little too much about things—like a lot of moms, I guess. But she's a great sport. She'd probably rather spend her vacations at home gardening, or maybe sitting beside some hotel pool reading a book; but she goes on camping trips with the rest of the family. All of us took a fifty-mile hike on the Appalachian Trail last summer. And the year before that the entire family canoed and camped for a week on the Au Sable River in Michigan."

Jennifer asked about the hiking and the canoeing and I told her about other trips I'd taken with Dad, when just the two of us got away for a weekend three or four times a year.

Sometime later Jennifer said, "You never did answer my question."

"I forgot what it was."

"Do you think you're more like your mom or your dad?"

"I don't know. I love them both."

"That's a different question. Which one are you most like?"

"I guess I'm a combination. I love to do the things Dad loves to do. I enjoy the satisfaction of having done something new and different. I like the feeling that comes from a challenge. But I'm not as naturally aggressive as he is. My personality is more like my mom's. I can be comfortable with a regular routine. And I'm fairly quiet and reserved in a group. So I am a combination. Does that make any sense?"

She nodded and her face looked thoughtful for a moment. In the silence I checked my watch. We'd been talking for two hours—it seemed more like two minutes.

"I haven't been watching the time," I said. "I'd better get you home. I've got to be at work early in the morning."

"Where do you work?" Jennifer asked.

So I told her as we drove about the part-time job I had on Saturday mornings, stocking shelves and checking inventory at a local hardware store. Nothing very glamorous about nuts and bolts and copper tubing. But I thought it was more fun than flipping burgers in a fast-food joint. The owner was a good boss who trusted and respected me enough to let me modify the inventory-control and pricing software on the store's computer.

I finished telling her about the job as we sat parked in her driveway. I guess I kept talking because I didn't want the date to end. Then an idea hit me.

"Were you going to that concert tomorrow night with the church youth group?" I asked.

"I'd planned on it," Jennifer said.

"Well, uh, I know it's a little late to ask," I said. "But would you go with me? If you aren't going with anyone else, I mean?"

I think she smiled. It was hard to see in the car, in the dark. I hoped she smiled. I did see her nod. "Sure," she said. "I'd like that a lot." I hoped she really meant it.

Walking her to the door I noticed how tall she was for a girl. And when she turned to face me on her front porch and said, "I had a real nice time tonight, Matt, thanks." Then I gave her a short good-night kiss. I'd never kissed a girl I didn't have to bend down to reach before. It seemed different. But natural at the same time.

Her lips were as warm as her hands had been. And that same shiver ran through me. "See you tomorrow night then," I said.

"What time?" she asked. When I looked at my watch she laughed. "What time tomorrow?"

I grinned. "It's almost tomorrow now. Just another half hour. But I suppose 12:01 A.M. would be a little early. Say I pick you up about seven again."

"See you then," she said. And she disappeared into the dark house.

Mom and Dad had already gone to bed when I got home. So I locked the door behind me and went to my room. But there was no way I could sleep. I kept replaying the evening in my mind.

It had been perfect. Except I probably talked too much. I'd never talked that much on any date before, let alone a first date. I vowed to let Jennifer do the talking the next time and I'd do the listening. But then I realized that she was the one who'd gotten me talking in the first place, and she'd listened as if she was interested in everything I said. Jennifer was different. Something about her drew me out. She made me think with her questions.

But mostly she made me feel . . . sort of excited and calm at the same time. Comfortable and uneasy. Warm, but shivery.

I wasn't exactly an expert on the subject. But as I thrashed around on my bed, I felt certain my diagnosis was probably accurate: *Matt Guthrie*, I said to myself, *I think you're falling in love*.

It felt good. Confusing, but good. I was lying there enjoying and trying to sort out the new feelings when I heard the voices from my parents' bedroom. They were louder than whispers, more like normal voices. But with their door closed I could only hear the tone of their words, not the words themselves. The conversation sounded intense.

I looked over at the radio clock beside my bed. It was 12:45 A.M. I wondered what my parents could be talking about so seriously at that hour.

But I didn't give it much thought. I was too busy reliving my evening and trying to decide what I would wear when I picked up Jennifer in just over eighteen hours.

I drifted off to sleep thinking I'd just spent the best day of my life. I never dreamed I was about to experience the worst.

CHAPTER

2

When I got home a little after noon, Dad was washing his car in the driveway. "I'll help if I can use the car again tonight," I told him, propping my ten-speed against the house.

"It's a deal," he said as he tossed me a wet rag.

It didn't take long before we were finished. "You hungry?" Dad asked as I dried the chrome around the headlights.

"Not really. Had a chili dog at the Dairy Queen on the way home."

"Want to shoot a few hoops? Maybe get creamed in a quick game of one on one?"

I grinned. "Why? Is Michael Jordan here?"

"No. Just an old guy who can still shoot a good enough jumper to beat you!"

I laughed. "Where is he? In the backyard trying to get loosened up?"

Dad smiled and shook his head. "Come on, hotshot, I'll show you right where he is."

When we got around back, I found the ball in the garage and closed the garage door. "Where's Mom?" I asked, taking a warm-up shot.

"She's spending the day over at your grandparents. She took Melissa and Mark with her. Said they'd be back around four."

We played a couple of games to twenty-one. Dad won the first one. Then I wore him down and took the second. For a forty-one-year-old guy, Dad was in great shape. He'd put up the backboard and goal when I was ten. I don't know how many thousand games we'd played; Mom used to predict we were going to wear all the concrete off the driveway before I left home for college. But that was less than a year and a half away now, and it looked like the concrete was going to last.

I'd been almost sixteen before I could stay with Dad in an all-out game, and we were still pretty even. So we were both dripping sweat when he suggested we knock off the one-on-one and shoot a game or two of "Horse."

"Sounds good to me," I gasped. I beat him two straight games. The second was easier than the first. He was either very tired or he'd lost his concentration. Finally he said, "I think you've had enough," walked over to the picnic table, and flopped down.

I took one more left-handed hook shot before he said, "Come here a minute, Matt. I've got something to tell you."

I retrieved the ball and walked over to take a seat. Dad didn't say anything for a minute. He suddenly looked older than I'd ever seen him look, and I knew something was wrong.

"I don't really know how to tell you this," he finally said. Something was very wrong; he was looking straight ahead, not at me. "So I'll just say it. I'm gonna be moving out of the house for a while. Your mom and I have been having a few problems lately and . . ."

It took a few seconds for the first sentence to register. Dad kept on talking and I stared at him. I saw his lips moving, but the words didn't make any sense. They crashed down on me like an avalanche. I felt like the screaming, panicked actors I'd seen on TV once in that old movie, "The Last Days of Pompeii," in one scene where the ground was heaving and shaking and the entire world seemed to come apart. *This can't be happening,* I thought numbly. *Not to me. Not to my dad and mom.* But the words kept coming.

"We've just been growing farther and farther apart. She's not happy, I'm not happy. I think the best thing for both of us, and for the family in the long run, is for us to separate for a while, to get a little time and space to sort things out."

I had to force the words out of my throat. "Mom agrees?"

"I'm gonna tell her as soon as she gets home today."

"She doesn't know?" I looked at him in a daze. *Why is he telling me?* I wondered.

"I don't think she'll be surprised," he said quietly. "I plan to tell Melissa and Mark tonight. That's why I wanted to tell you now. It'll be hard for them to understand. Maybe you can help."

How can I help them understand what I don't understand myself? I thought. But I didn't say any-thing. There were no words inside me. There was nothing inside but a screaming, panicking multitude of thoughts and an aching emptiness.

"I'm sorry, Matt. I can't tell you how sorry I am. I still love you. All of you." His voice sounded raspy and choked. But I didn't look over at him.

We sat for a long time in silence. Finally Dad got up, "I'm gonna take a shower," he said. "You comin' inside?"

I just shook my head. His sad, tired voice seemed to reach out to me from miles away. "I'm sorry. You'll never know how sorry, Matt."

But a million "sorry"s couldn't rebuild Pompeii.

I sat like a statue on that picnic table bench for another half hour. But my mind was racing back and forth in search of some understanding. Nothing. Then I tried to think back to some clue I'd missed. Some minor tremor that should have warned me of the coming disaster. *Nothing*.

Finally I had to move. I had to get away.

I sprinted out the driveway and over two blocks to the Thomas Jefferson High School football field where I ran around the track again and again and again. I don't know how many laps I made before my lungs and my legs screamed so loud in pain that I had to slow to a walk. But the physical pain did nothing to ease the deeper hurt.

When I finally quit alternately walking and running around the track, I walked over and collapsed on the bleachers. I didn't want to go home yet because I didn't want to be there when Mom got back. Rationally, I knew I had nothing to do with what was going to happen. It wasn't my fault or my decision. But knowing what Dad was going to say to Mom made me feel as if I was a part of some terrible conspiracy. And rational or not, I felt guilty for knowing, for being unable to stop what was happening.

It was nearly five before I headed home. Mom's car

sat in the driveway. I felt even guiltier slipping around to the back door, but I couldn't face her. Not yet.

It was no use. I saw her the second I stepped in the back door. She was standing at the kitchen sink, staring out the window. When she turned to look at me I saw that her face was puffy and red. And I knew the instant our eyes met that she knew—and she knew I knew.

Looking back, I probably should have said something. But I didn't know what to say. I could have at least walked over and given her a hug. But the thought never even crossed my mind. All I could think of was how awful I felt to be standing there, looking at her and knowing. . . .

"I gotta make a phone call," I said. And then I hurried out of the kitchen and headed upstairs.

Jennifer answered the phone. "Hi," I said. "This is Matt."

"Hi."

"I called to say I'm sorry, but I'm not going to be going to that concert tonight after all. Something, uh, came up, uh, with my family. I'm sorry."

"Oh, OK," she said. I could tell from the way she said it that I needed to say something more. But I couldn't. "See you tomorrow night at church then?" she asked.

"I don't know. Maybe," I said. "I gotta go."

"Bye."

A long hot shower loosened some of my aching muscles. But it didn't do a thing for the knot in my guts.

I'd just finished pulling on a T-shirt and a clean pair of running shorts when Dad called up the stairs. Melissa and Mark were already in the family room when I got there. Mom sat in one of the easy chairs with a Kleenex wadded tightly in her hand. Dad sat on the edge of the hearth.

I stopped and leaned against the side of the doorjamb between the kitchen and the family room. But Dad motioned me in to take a place on the couch between my brother and sister.

It didn't take long. But then I guess there wasn't much point in prolonging the pain. Mom sat in her chair, staring at her lap. Dad did all the explaining—saying some of what he'd said to me, but trying to simplify it for the younger kids. "I have something to tell you that makes me very sad," he said, looking at the three of us. "I want you to know that I love you all very much. I expect this will be hard for you to understand. But I've decided it'd be best for me and your mother, for all of us really, if I lived somewhere else for a while. . . ."

I felt Melissa flinch beside me and when I glanced toward her I saw she was biting her lower lip the way she does when she's getting agitated. Mark looked more puzzled than upset by what he was hearing. He was the first one to speak when Dad finally paused.

"Where will you live if you don't live here with us? Will you stay in a tent like we do on vacation?"

Dad smiled a little and shook his head. "I'll probably stay in a hotel for a little while. And then I'll try to get an apartment somewhere in town."

"Then we can come and see you?" Mark wanted to know.

"Of course, you can," Dad said, stepping to the couch and squatting down to Mark's eye level. "Wherever I live, I promise it won't be far away. You can come and visit anytime. And I'll come and visit you.

I'll still be your dad. And I'll still love you just as much as I always have." He looked at me and Melissa and then back to Mark. "We'll still be a family."

"Some family!" I muttered. I didn't think. The words, more an emotion really, just burst out. And I regretted them even before Dad shot me a pained look that said, "Don't make this any harder, please!"

"Can I go play outside now?" Mark asked.

"Sure," Dad said, looking a little surprised. And a bit relieved.

I turned and watched Mark go, wondering for a moment if he didn't understand what was happening. Or maybe he was only trying to act as if everything was normal in a six-year-old's hope that pretending could make something true. But the moment Mark disappeared out the door, Melissa began to blubber. "D-d-d-does this m-mean . . ." her whole body convulsed into a sob before she blurted out the rest, "that you and mom are g-going to get a . . . d-divorce?" She looked at Dad and then at Mom.

"All it means," Dad said, "is that we're going to be separated. For awhile."

He didn't say no. I'm sure Melissa noticed that too. "I don't believe this," she screamed as she ran from the room, out into the hall, and then pounded up the stairs. Her bedroom door slammed a few seconds later.

"I'd better go talk to her," Dad said, moving toward the door.

"No," Mom said, standing quickly. "I'll talk to her."

Dad let Mom go. And the two of us were alone again. "I've got to be going," I said, hurrying to escape the room. Dad didn't say anything. But I could feel his eyes on my back as I walked out.

I spent the rest of the night in my room with the radio

on. But I didn't hear the music. At one point I thought I heard Dad's car backing out of the driveway. But mostly I just kept hearing the words over and over in my mind: *I'm gonna be moving out . . . your mom and I have been having a few problems . . . I'm gonna be moving out . . . she's not happy and I'm not happy . . . it'll be best for all of us . . . I'm gonna be moving out. . . .*

And I prayed. Harder than I'd ever prayed about anything in my life. It seemed like I prayed for hours. But all I remember saying was, "God, please don't let this happen. Do something to stop it. Please, God!"

CHAPTER

3

As consciousness seeped through me the next morning, I felt the relief you feel when you waken from a bad dream. But by the time I'd rolled over, put my feet on the floor, and sat up, the relief had drained away to dread. It wasn't a dream.

I pulled on a pair of pants and went to my window. Dad's car wasn't in the driveway.

Walking down the hall and past the open door of Mom and Dad's bedroom I noticed their bed was made, as if it hadn't been slept in. When I got downstairs and walked into the kitchen, I saw why.

Mom sat staring at the kitchen table. The unopened morning newspaper and a cup of cold coffee, over half-full, sat in front of her. She looked like hell. Or like someone who'd spent the night there. A long strand of brown hair hung down over her red-splotched face. The dark circles under her eyes were streaked with mascara. She looked up as I walked into the kitchen.

"I don't feel up to going to church today," she said. "But you can drive Melissa and Mark if you want. What would you like for breakfast?"

"Don't worry about it, Mom," I said, walking to the refrigerator. "I'll just get out some juice and yogurt for everybody."

She didn't protest. Mark walked in a few seconds later, already dressed for church and declaring, "I'm hungry."

"We're just having yogurt," I announced as Melissa trailed in behind Mark, still wearing her pajamas. "And we're not going to church this morning. Mom isn't feeling good."

Mark looked at Mom for a moment before walking to the counter and picking up a carton of strawberry-banana yogurt. "Then can I watch TV this morning?" he asked.

"Sure," Mom said. She didn't look up.

Melissa picked up her yogurt, got a spoon out of the silverware drawer, and headed back upstairs to her room without a word. I leaned against the counter and slowly stirred the blueberries up from the bottom of my yogurt.

Mom just sat there, staring at the table, her eyes glazed. She reminded me of those films we saw in my first aid class of accident victims in shock. You're supposed to make them lie down and then cover them with blankets or something to keep them warm. I'd made an A in first aid. But it was a sick helpless feeling standing there, realizing I didn't know the first thing to do to help my own mother.

I guess I was in shock, too. I went to school that week, but I was only going through the motions. All I really learned was how strange it feels to watch everyone else's lives go blissfully on when yours has come to a crashing halt. I also learned how easy it is to hide in a crowd of two thousand students. I went to classes, did my assignments, greeted my friends in the hallway, and listened to all the excited chatter about summer and the end of school just two weeks away. But not one person really saw me, saw what I was feeling inside. Maybe it was because I didn't let them. But they weren't really looking either.

Like Wednesday in study hall. Just before the bell rang I slid into my seat at the table with the same three guys I'd sat with every day all year. Jeff Rutledge, who was also my best friend and went to my church, asked me if I wanted to play a game of chess. Mr. Wilson, our study hall monitor, let us play as long as we didn't talk and disturb the people around us.

"Not today," I said. "Got too much calculus homework. And I don't want to take it home."

So he started a game with Allen Finnan. Pete Swanson watched and waited to take on the winner. They talked quietly among themselves; Allen was telling Pete where he thought he could find a summer job. And then they all laughed as Jeff recounted something that had happened in his Lit class earlier that morning.

I looked up from my calculus book fifteen minutes later to see that Jeff had captured both of Allen's bishops, a rook, and a knight. And he was closing in for the kill. Five minutes later, Pete and Allen changed seats and a new game started.

None of my friends seemed to notice that the piece of paper in front of me was still blank. I stared at my open book for minutes on end without seeing anything.

Everything seemed so strange, so detached from

me. It was as if my friends, calculus, and everything else in the world was in some sort of parallel universe. They were there, but I wasn't. It was like looking at someone else through a two-way mirror.

Thursday, Dad came by to take all three of us kids out to eat. He honked his horn from the driveway instead of coming to the door. Mark raced to the car and threw his arms around Dad. Melissa climbed silently into the back seat with Mark, and I slid in next to Dad. It seemed like more than five days since I'd seen him.

We stopped at a steak house, and we'd no sooner placed our orders and gotten situated in a booth than Mark asked, "Do you know when you're coming home yet?"

Dad shook his head. "No," he admitted. "But I did find a place to stay. There's an opening the first of June at the Beaujolais Apartments. One of those complexes out near Kmart. So I'll be close by. You'll be able to call me or come see me anytime you like. I'll be moving in next weekend."

When there didn't seem to be anything more to be said on that subject, he asked: "What's been happening at school this week?" Mark told him about a special dinosaur party he'd had in his class. Melissa reported very briefly on a field trip to a museum down in the city. And I said, "It's just the usual year-end wrap-up at school."

"Got a lot of finals next week?" Dad asked.

I shook my head. "Just unit tests. No real comprehensive finals. It's been a light semester."

The meal dragged on painfully long after that. There's only so many comments to be made about steak, potatoes, and the salad bar.

When he pulled in the drive and stopped, Dad said, "I'm afraid I won't be seeing you guys next week. I leave Monday for a sales meeting, and I won't be back in town till Friday. But I'll call when I get back, and we'll go out again. Maybe catch a movie or do something after we eat next time. OK?"

He kissed Mark and Melissa good-bye, and they headed into the house. Then he put his hand on my shoulder. "I know this is hard for you, Matt. It's hard for me, too. It's gonna take some time. For all of us. But it'll get easier. You'll see."

I nodded. But I didn't believe it. Things could never be better until we were all together again.

The second week was nearly a Xerox copy of the first. We skipped church again. But I prayed the same prayer every night before I fell asleep and every morning when I woke up: "Please God, you can stop this. Please!" And every day the routine of school raced toward the year's conclusion.

Every morning Mom looked as if she hadn't slept at all. She seldom smiled, and when she did, it only seemed to underline the sadness in her eyes. She was a picture of what I'd always thought of when I heard the word "depressed." She functioned on one level —she fixed meals, did the laundry, and cleaned house. But only in a mindless sort of way.

One day when I got home from school she was sitting in the upstairs hallway, the contents of the linen closet spread on the floor around her. "I've been wanting to reorganize this closet for over a year," she explained. I nodded a response and stepped over a pile of towels to get into my room.

But the extra effort it took to go beyond the essential tasks of daily family survival proved a little too much for Mom that day. I was just finishing up my last geometry homework problem when I heard her shut the linen closet door and then knock on mine. "Would you mind running out and getting a bucket of fried chicken for supper, Matt? I don't feel much like cooking tonight."

I got home from work on Saturday about noon and headed up to my room to put on a pair of shorts. My parents' bedroom door was closed when I passed it, but I thought I heard Mom inside— crying. Heading back down the hall after I changed, I stopped outside the door and listened to her sobbing. After a minute or so, I knocked softly on the door.

The crying quieted and I heard Mom say, "Yes?"

"It's me, Matt. Are you OK?" I heard the bed springs. It sounded like she was getting up. "You can come in, Matt," she said.

I opened the door to see her sitting on the edge of her bed. Stepping into the room I saw immediately what had prompted this bout of tears. Across the room behind her, the sliding door to the closet stood open. Dad's end was cleared out. All his clothes were gone.

"Your dad came by this morning to pick up some of his things," she said, stating the obvious. "He's moving into an apartment today."

"I know."

She shrugged. "He told me last week he'd be coming by. I guess I was hoping while he was gone to San Francisco, he'd change his . . ." As her words died, so did a big part of my hope.

"It'll be OK, Mom. It'll just take a little time." I said the words with so little feeling that I felt guilty. And I wondered if God really considers it a lie when you try to say something comforting even though you don't know if you believe it.

Mom looked up at me, smiled that pathetic smile she'd resorted to recently, and said, "I hope you're right, dear."

I took a walk through the house. Besides his clothes, Dad had taken a few boxes of books from the little room in the basement that he used as a home office. A lamp and an old recliner were also gone from the room. And on the wall above the desk, there was a faint rectangle where the paint seemed a lighter green. It was where he'd always hung a photo of the old barn on the farm where he'd grown up in Minnesota. He'd also taken the antique fishing reel that had been his grandfather's. I almost missed that; it wasn't in it's usual place on the mantle in the family room. All in all, he hadn't taken much. Yet the house seemed strangely empty.

Dad certainly hadn't taken enough to furnish an apartment. I tried to imagine a bare room with a pile of books sitting next to a recliner. It seemed like he'd get pretty lonely in a hurry. Maybe I could go and stay with him. In my mind I told myself it wasn't practical. But in my heart I felt that if I were with him, maybe I could understand. Maybe I could help him understand.

I lay awake a long time that night. Thinking. Hurting. Worrying about Dad. And Mom. Especially Mom. As depressed as she'd been before, how was she going to cope now?

And I prayed. Not the same prayer I'd been praying day after day, night after night, for two weeks. God hadn't answered that one. He hadn't stopped anything. The nightmare kept right on going, right on growing. I was ready to give up on that prayer.

This time I prayed: "Why, God? Why is this happening to my family? Show me why. Tell me why." It was
the first time in my life I'd ever prayed a prayer like
that, demanding an answer from God.

From the time I was a little kid, I had believed that
God loved me—that he was good and wanted only
good things for me. My parents had always taught us
that. I remember Dad telling me, time after time as I
grew up, "You know how much your mother and I love
you. As hard as it may be to believe, God loves you
even more than we do." I never doubted it. I remember
I was only eight when, riding home from church one
Sunday, I told my parents I wanted to pray and ask
Jesus to be my Savior. And I did it, right there in the car
as we drove. Mom cried. And when we got home Dad
gave me a big hug and told me how proud he was of
me. "That's the most important decision you can ever
make," he told me.

And only a couple of years ago, near the end of my
ninth-grade year, after a special service at church when
I went down front to pray and tell God that I wanted to
live my whole life for him, both Mom and Dad had
been there, supporting me.

Of course, we'd had our differences. Seventh and
eighth grades had been rough. I'd wanted more
independence than my parents were ready to give me.
But we worked through that. And I never doubted they
loved me. Or that I loved them. They were always
there. Not just for me, but for a lot of other people.
They were at church every time the doors opened.
They taught Sunday school. They volunteered with
Scouts. Dad coached Little League baseball. I was
always so proud of them. My friends thought they

were great. People at church thought they were great. And so did I. We had a great Christian family.

I could even remember how upset my parents were when Tim Adam's parents got a divorce. I think I was about ten at the time. But I've never forgotten how Dad and Mom sat me down and explained what had happened. They talked about how important families and marriages are to God, and how sad God is when something like that happens because it hurts so many people.

So I had a lot of reasons for being so surprised at what was happening to my own family. It seemed impossible to understand. I guess that's why I began to pray: *Why, God?*

I finally fell asleep without an answer to that prayer either.

Mom surprised me the next morning. By the time I got downstairs, she was dressed for church. Her hair was curled for the first time in two weeks. And if there were any tell-tale splotches on her face, her makeup covered them. "We have to leave in twenty-five minutes, Matt," she said. "You better hurry."

I went back to youth group meeting that night. Jennifer was there, but I sat on the other side of the room with Kevin Simpson, another good friend of ours. Afterward, I was heading out to the parking lot alone when Jennifer trotted up behind me, her red hair bouncing on her shoulders.

"Can I talk to you a minute, Matt? I haven't seen you the last couple of weeks."

I turned to face her.

"I heard about your parents, Matt. And I wanted to tell you how sorry I am."

"I guess everyone knows then, huh?"

"I don't know about everyone. Evidently your mom told Shelley Simpson's mom this morning. Shelley told me because she knew I'd been wondering why I hadn't heard from you since we went out two weeks ago."

"So now you know why."

"Look, Matt." She reached out and put her hand on my arm. Her touch was as warm as I remembered. "I know my experience is a little different. I was only eleven when my parents split up. And they'd been fighting so much for as long as I could remember that it was something of a relief when my father finally left. But it still hurt. And I remember what that pain was like.

"So I know a little about what you're going through. And I want you to know I'm sorry because I care and I understand what—"

I pulled my arm out from under her hand. "You only think you understand!" My outburst surprised me, but not enough to keep me from saying, "You're right when you say your situation was different. You don't know my parents. They aren't like yours. So you don't understand how I feel! You couldn't!"

With that I whirled and headed for my car. Jennifer was still standing where I left her when I pulled out of the parking lot and accelerated down the street.

I hadn't driven a mile before I knew I'd made a stupid mistake. She'd only wanted to help. She'd cared enough to come out and talk to me. No one else had even acknowledged that anything might be wrong. She'd been trying to show her concern, and I'd reacted like a real jerk.

At the next corner I made a U-turn and headed back. But by the time I reached the church, the parking lot was empty. I drove home feeling worse than I'd felt at any time in the past two weeks. If that was possible.

CHAPTER

4

The school year ended on Tuesday. I walked out of the
building at the end of the day with a crowd of my junior
friends: Jeff, Allen, Pete, Jeff's girlfriend Tanya, and a
few others. "We're seniors now!" Allen shouted.
Several people cheered.

I smiled in response to their mini-celebration. But I
couldn't really anticipate the coming Fall. Two and a
half months is too big a jump in thinking when you
don't know how you're going to cope with today. Or
what's going to happen tomorrow.

Wednesday I got up early and dressed for my first
full day of work at Hagstrom's Hardware. When I got
down to the kitchen, Mom had my breakfast about
ready and was poring over the morning paper.

"Matt, what size tires does the station wagon take?"
she asked.

"I don't remember. But you can check by looking at
the tires. The size is written right on the sidewall.
Why?"

"Because Sears is having a big sale on steel-belted radials and I thought maybe I ought to get a couple of new tires. I think the two on the front are the same ones that came with the car," Mom said.

"Shouldn't you . . . ," I stopped without adding *ask Dad*. She evidently didn't want to do that. It's just that I'd never known my mom to do anything more with a car than fill it up when the gas got low. The cars had always been Dad's responsibility. When either vehicle needed work, he'd take it in and talk with the mechanic. Or he'd do the routine maintenance himself.

Mom guessed what I was thinking. "It's about time I learned something about cars," she said. "I was thinking maybe I ought to have them rotate the tires and align the front-end while they're at it. What do you think?"

"Sure," I replied, a little surprised Mom knew there was such a thing as a front-end alignment. "But why don't you wait until I get off work this afternoon and I'll ride to the mall with you to get the tires."

Mom shook her head and smiled. "Thanks, anyway. But I think I can handle it. And before I let any mechanic talk me into an engine overhaul, I'll check with you, OK?"

I had to grin. "Be sure and do that," I said.

Riding to work on my bike, I realized my mom had definitely emerged from her two weeks in shock. Going to church on Sunday had been the first clue. But her plan to go out and get tires for the car was practically a declaration of determination to take charge of her life again.

It felt good to have Mom back. And over the next few days I marveled at and appreciated her determination to restore a feeling of normality to the house, to our family. She smiled more. And from what I saw—or more accurately, what I didn't see—she cried less.

Sunday afternoon we even made a family outing to my grandparents' home for a big Sunday dinner and a lazy summer afternoon of relaxation. We've done that a lot over the years. As kids, we always looked forward to Grandma's big meals and her homemade desserts. And afterwards, in cold weather anyway, we'd head for the basement to play shuffleboard or Ping-Pong. When it was nice out we'd explore the woods bordering the back of my grandparents' yard. As I got a little older, I spent a lot of Sunday afternoons in Grandpa's den, listening to him and Dad talk as we watched a ball game on television.

This particular Sunday, Grandpa and I did all the talking during a cable broadcast of a game between the Chicago Cubs and the L.A. Dodgers. I love my grandparents very much. So I enjoyed the visit. But as the afternoon wore on I felt a growing uneasiness that was very different from the warm, comfortable feelings I usually experienced on our family visits. I'd expected Dad's absence to affect the afternoon, to make it awkward or sad or something. But it wasn't that.

It wasn't until we were on the thirty-minute drive home that night that I pinpointed the reason for my feelings. It wasn't Dad's absence that seemed so strange; it was the fact that no one had even mentioned him or his absence all afternoon.

I knew for a fact that Grandma and Grandpa loved my dad. He'd been their son-in-law for over nineteen years. But they hadn't mentioned his name all day; they hadn't once verbally acknowledged his absence. None of us had. It was as if we'd all entered into an unspoken conspiracy to pretend normality. I was part of it. And that was the source of the uneasiness eating at my subconscious.

It seemed as though everyone joined the conspiracy.

One night when Jeff dropped by and picked me up to go for some pizza, he raised the subject. "Sorry about your parents, Matt. It's gotta be rough." When I didn't say anything he asked, "Are you doing OK?"

"Yeah," I lied. "I'm OK. I think it'll work out; they just need a little time." Perhaps the last part wasn't really a lie. Dad had come over a couple of times and he and Mom had gone out in the kitchen and talked for a long time. I don't know what they were talking about, but as long as they were talking it was something.

But after that night Jeff didn't ask about my parents again. The longer the separation went on the more awkward it was to talk about, I guess. Not one of my other friends asked about my dad or even mentioned him when they were over shooting hoops or watching videos. My boss, Mr. Hagstrom, who'd known my dad for years, carefully avoided any reference to what I'm sure he knew was happening. During meals, Mom and Melissa and I found other things to talk about.

There were only a couple of exceptions to this conspiracy. Every couple of mornings Mark would come down to breakfast and ask, "Is this the day Dad is coming home?" And Mom would take a deep breath and look very sad as she'd reply, "I don't think so, honey."

The other exception was Gary Maxwell, the youth minister of our church. He stopped by one night and asked if I'd like to go out for a few minutes and get some ice cream. We talked some about my job, about the prospects of the National League baseball season, and about a few of my friends from church. After a while he plunged into the real reason for his visit by saying, "I heard about your dad moving out, Matt. I wanted to let you know I'm sorry about that. And if there's ever any time you want to talk about it, or about your feelings, I'm glad to talk. Or just listen."

"Thanks," I said. "But I think everything's going to work out in time. And I'm doing OK." I was even more uneasy talking about the situation than I was pretending everything was normal. And that bothered me.

Even Dad seemed to be avoiding reality. He'd take Mark, Melissa, and me out a couple of times a week. And the minute we got in his car he'd ask what we'd been doing since the last time we'd been together. It was as if he thought we could just take up where we'd left off the time before.

Father's Day nearly cracked the conspiracy. Nothing was normal. Instead of going to church as a family and coming home to a big family dinner, the three of us kids went out for dinner with Dad late that afternoon. When we got in the car, I gave him a funny Father's Day card and Melissa pinned a red carnation boutonniere to the lapel of his sport coat before she gave him a big kiss on the cheek. Mark handed him a card he'd drawn and colored himself.

On the front was a crude drawing of an airplane flying high in the sky and pulling a sign on which Mark and lettered: "Happy Father's Day."

"That's really nice, Mark," Dad said. "What famous artist did you get to do this drawing?"

"I drew it myself."

Dad shook his head in pretend disbelief. "I can't believe a six-year-old could draw such a fine card. But it was sure nice that you have a big sister to help you write the message." He looked at Melissa who grinned.

"I wrote it myself, too," Mark declared proudly. "I did it all by myself."

"Really?" Dad asked. "It's terrific."

"Look inside," Mark demanded.

"There's more?" Dad opened the card. There was another plane pulling another sign that said, "To the best dad in the world." And down at the bottom of the page was a picture of a house with a face at the window and a little comic book type of balloon coming out of the window. Inside the balloon were the words, "I miss you. Love, Mark."

"Lissa helped me spell the words," Mark said. "But I did it all myself."

"Well, it's terrific!" Dad said, pulling Mark into his arms and holding him tight for a long time. After Mark climbed into the backseat and we headed for the restaurant, Dad stayed very quiet. And as he drove, he rubbed at his eyes a couple of times like something was in them. I don't think Melissa or Mark noticed. But I knew. And despite the casual small talk around the restaurant table, despite the smiles, despite the little speech Dad made about how lucky he was to have three great kids, none of us could really pretend that this was a normal Father's Day.

Lying in bed that night, I thought about Mark's card. And about Dad's reaction. Maybe the separation was beginning to get to him. And I told myself I was going to quit pretending. I was going to admit, at least to myself, that I missed my dad, too. I was going to resign from the conspiracy. As awkward and painful as my feelings were, I was going to face them, feel them, and not deny them any longer. If we all did that, maybe this whole crazy episode would come to an end.

Facing one set of emotions forced me to think about another. The day after Father's Day I decided to call Jennifer. I'd almost called her as soon as I'd gotten home the night I'd blown up at her. But I'd decided to wait until I could see her face-to-face. Then I was at my grandparents' the next Sunday night and she'd gone on vacation with her mom. By the time a couple of weeks had gone by, I felt so bad about putting off the apology for so long, that it seemed easier to put it off another week.

I dialed and listened to the phone ring. Jennifer answered.

"Hi, Jennifer, this is Matt Guthrie," I said.

"Oh, hi." There was a touch of surprise in her voice.

"I was wondering if you were going to be home this evening."

"I don't have any plans," she said, her voice wary.

"Would it be all right if I drove over for a few minutes to talk?"

There was a pause. "I guess so," she replied.

"See you in thirty minutes then."

"OK."

"'Bye."

Click. Not exactly an enthusiastic invitation. But then the last time she'd seen me I'd blown up at her and driven away in a huff.

When I got there, we sat on the swing on her front porch, the smell of lilac heavy and sweet in the warm evening air. "I basically came over to apologize," I said. "To say I'm sorry for snapping at you like I did that night at church. You must have thought I acted like a real jerk."

"Yeah, I guess you did."

"You don't have to be so quick to agree."

"It's been more than three weeks, I don't think that's so quick," she responded.

"Hey, I'm sorry about that, too. I should have apologized sooner."

"I was angry that night. Then I got really ticked when you didn't call to apologize."

"I'm sorry," I said again.

"Let's just forget it," she said. "I guess I could have been a little more sensitive in . . ."

I shook my head. "You were just trying to show your concern. My reaction was my fault. You were the first person to say anything and I didn't know how to react."

"I guess I shouldn't hold that against you. I remember how . . . I'm sorry, there I go again."

"It's OK," I said.

"How's your job going?" she asked, changing the subject. So we talked about that for a while. I asked about her vacation with her mom, and she told me about that.

"Would you be free on Saturday night?" I asked at a break in the conversation. "Maybe we could catch a movie and then get something to eat and talk."

"I'm sorry," Jennifer said. "I'm baby-sitting for the neighbors on Saturday."

"Friday?"

"I've got plans for Friday already. Maybe some other time, OK?"

My heart sank. I'd heard that line before. "Yeah, sure. Some other time."

I guess she realized what I was thinking, because she added, "I mean it, Matt. I'd be glad to go out some other time. I really do have plans this time. I wish I didn't."

"You're not going to just happen to be washing your

hair or cleaning out your sock drawer the next time I ask you?"

She grinned and shook her head. "No. I promise."

"How 'bout a movie next Monday?"

"Oh, no," she said gravely, "that's the night I have to paste in the little corner tabs in my photo album."

"I knew it!" I exclaimed.

She laughed. "Monday's fine."

"Monday it will be th—, no, wait. I can't do it Monday. My little brother's got a T-Ball game that night. And I can't miss it. I promised him."

"T-Ball sounds more entertaining than a lot of movies. If it'd be all right, I mean. If it's not just going to be a family thing."

"That'd be great if you're sure you'd really want to come. We could still go out and get something to eat afterward."

"Sounds good," she said. And I began counting the hours till Monday night.

One night later that week, Melissa knocked on the door of my room. I told her to come in and she shut the door behind her. "Can we talk?"

"Sure. What about?"

"Well," she began, "a month from tomorrow is Mom's and Dad's anniversary. It's their twentieth."

"Yeah, I know." I'd tried not to think about it.

"Don't you think we ought to plan something? Maybe invite Dad over for a special family barbecue or something. You could grill some steaks. I could bake a cake."

"I don't think so, Melissa. People who are separated don't usually want to celebrate their anniversary."

"But I thought maybe if we could get them together, we could all have a good time and—"

"Forget it. It's a dumb idea!"

Melissa began to cry.

"I'm sorry, Melissa. I shouldn't have said that. It's actually a very . . . thoughtful idea. It just wouldn't work."

"How do you know?"

I tried to think of an explanation. "I don't think you'd get either of them to agree to it. If they say no, it'll only make them and you feel bad. If one agreed and the other didn't, they'd both feel bad about that. Even if they both agreed, it would be so awkward that we'd all feel bad. So I don't think there's any way it could work out the way you want it to."

Melissa sniffled. "We've got to do something. If we don't they could get a divorce!"

"Nobody's talking about a divorce yet."

"Yet! Right."

"I think the only thing we can do is try to give them time to work out their problems." I could see by Melissa's expression she wasn't convinced. "It's their decision, their marriage. We can't force them to do anything."

Several thoughts were running through my mind as I talked to her. *If we push, then they might have to take a stand and say no. If they say no too often, it gets easier and easier and the decision could be made. The wrong decision. No, we can't force anything.*

But Melissa's suggestion got me thinking. *If there was some reason they had to be together, and if we all had a good time, maybe . . .* There might be something. But definitely not the anniversary thing.

"Please forget the anniversary celebration. OK, Melissa?"

"OK," she conceded. "But I'm not giving up on our

family, even if you are!" She jerked the door open and stormed out.

I almost went after her, to tell her I knew how she felt and that I wasn't giving up. But I didn't.

CHAPTER

5

I picked Jennifer up about six Monday evening and headed back home to collect Mom, Melissa, and Mark for the ride to the game. It was the first time Jennifer had met my family. But I think she made a good impression, especially with Mark when she exclaimed how his miniature major league replica uniform made him look just like a real pro.

We got to the park early and found seats right behind the bench while Mark's team warmed up. Mom and Melissa sat on the bottom bleacher and Jennifer and I sat right behind them.

Five minutes before game time, Dad walked up. Mark ran over and gave him a big hug, and then I introduced him to Jennifer. He grinned and said, "I know Matt tends to be a bit on the stingy side, but this looks to me like a very inexpensive date."

Jennifer laughed. "He did say something about getting a bite to eat after the game."

"Hmmm," Dad responded. "Hold him to it. And

just in case, make him buy you a popcorn and a coke over at the concession stand." He grinned at me.

Dad had told Mark he'd be at the game, so I hadn't been surprised to see him. But I was a little surprised when he sat down on the bottom row of the bleachers beside Mom. I guess, when I think about it, it would have seemed pretty strange if he'd gone and sat somewhere else away from the family. It just struck me as I sat in the row behind my parents that it was the first time I'd seen them together in over a month.

They didn't really say much. At least not to each other. But they both cheered whenever Matt got to bat and each time he touched the ball in the field.

T-Ball for six-year-olds isn't exactly the most stimulating spectator sport in the world. A team's turn at bat ends after three outs (which almost never happens) or after everyone gets a chance to bat. Most players hit ground balls. And most ground balls roll until they stop and someone picks up the ball and throws it past everyone else. It was pretty funny really, but we all cheered like crazy. And every time Mark walked up to the plate he'd turn and wave at us before he took his first swing.

By the middle of the second inning, I think most of the people watching felt like the little boy on Mark's team who yelled down the length of the bench, "Is it almost over yet, coach? When do we get our snack?"

Mark actually fielded a grounder at shortstop and forced the runner at second. And he got three legitimate singles, so he was thrilled. When the game was over, Dad gave him a big hug, and we all congratulated him on his playing.

"We need to be getting home," Mom finally said. "Matt and Jennifer are going out."

"I'll drop everyone home," Dad said to me. "Then you two can get on with your plans from here."

"But . . . ," I looked at Mom.

"Go on," she said. "That'll be fine."

"Awriiight!" Mark exclaimed as we all began walking toward the parking lot.

"Thanks for coming tonight," I said to Jennifer as we waited for our order at McDougal's. "I'd forgotten how long T-ball games can be."

She smiled. "The game was a riot. All those little kids. I enjoyed it. And I'm glad I got to meet your family."

The order came and we started to eat.

"Your parents are nice. I liked them both."

I didn't say anything.

"Matt, I'm sorry. I didn't mean to bring up . . ."

I shook my head. "It's OK. I don't want you to feel like you have to avoid the subject of my parents. I'm actually a little tired of having everyone avoid the subject."

She changed the subject anyway. "I think your little brother is really cute."

"He liked you, too," I said.

"Well, I think it's really nice that your whole family cared enough to go to his game. It obviously meant a lot to him."

"My parents have always been supportive any time any of us kids have been involved in anything. So I'm glad we could all be there for Mark tonight." I paused for moment and added, "I expected him to be the one most affected by what's happening in our family. So far Mark is the one who seems to be accepting things the best."

"Maybe . . . ," Jennifer hesitated as if she was trying

to decide what to say. "My little sister was about Mark's age when my parents first separated. She acted so normal for the first couple of months that I wondered if she even knew Dad had gone.

"Then one day she was playing outside and just disappeared. Mom went out to call her for supper and she was gone. So was her little bike with the training wheels. I remember riding my own bike up and down our subdivision looking for her. I was so scared.

"The police finally called about ten o'clock that night. They'd found her in front of a convenience store over five miles from our house." Jennifer's voice tightened up. "She told the police . . . that she . . . that she didn't think anyone in her family loved her any more. And she was looking for another place to live." Tears were rolling down Jennifer's cheeks at the memory. She continued after a few seconds. "So you never know what little kids are thinking."

"I'll remember that. Thanks."

There was another long pause in the conversation before Jennifer asked, "What about your sister?"

"Melissa? I'm not sure." I told her about Melissa's anniversary idea.

"I was just a little younger than she is when my parents split up," Jennifer said. "The sudden peace and quiet after all those years of fighting was a welcome relief. But I still remember how much it hurt to know that my father was gone. I didn't miss the shouting he and my mother used to do. But I missed him."

Jennifer fell silent for a minute or so. Then she said, quietly, thoughtfully, "I've thought a lot about it the past few years. And I've decided that a family divorce, or even a separation, is a lot like a death in the family— only worse. You not only lose someone, or lose a relationship you had, but there's no one to understand, to give you permission to grieve and help you get over it.

"And as much as I was glad to have the fighting over with, I think I spent most of my time for the next six months trying to dream up some scheme that could get my parents back together and make everything right between them."

As I walked her up to her door, Jennifer apologized for talking so much about her own family. "I didn't mean to make it such a heavy time."

"It's OK," I tried to assure her. "You helped me realize I need to be more sensitive to Mark's feelings. Melissa's too. And I had a good time."

"Me, too," she said.

I leaned toward her to give her a nice long good-night kiss. After just a second or two she pulled away.

"See you Sunday night?" she asked, opening the door.

"Got any plans for Saturday night?"

"No."

"How about that movie we didn't go to this past weekend?"

"Great," she said. And when the door closed, I turned and practically skipped to the car.

But when I pulled into the driveway at home a few minutes later and saw that Dad's car wasn't still there, I couldn't help feeling disappointment. Seeing my parents together again at the game had convinced me we just needed time—and a few more opportunities like T-ball games.

But time seemed to be playing tricks that summer. On the one hand, the weeks raced by. One day it was the fourth of July and the next thing I knew it was the first of August. At the same time, a lot of individual days dragged on and on. Like the separation. And like the silence I felt whenever I'd lie in my bed at night and beg God to do something—to change Dad's mind, to bring him home, or at least to help me understand why this was happening.

Dad came to most of Mark's ball games. And he'd get together with all three of us kids at least once a week, usually twice. While the times we had with him gradually became less strained as we all got used to the routine, they never got to the point of feeling normal.

No matter what we did with Dad, no matter how much fun we had, no matter how much we laughed, I could never quite forget that it was all going to end in a few hours. We'd go home and he'd go back to his apartment. The visits were only distractions, sort of mini-vacations from reality. And like all vacations, no matter how great they are, you know they've got to come to an end. You have to go back home, and life goes on. Only Dad didn't go home with us, and life went on without him.

It wasn't as if Dad dropped out of our lives. He lived only a couple of miles away. "Give me a call anytime you want to talk," he'd said. Mark called him every other day or so, just to say hi or to tell him good night. If Dad wasn't in when he called, Mark would leave a message on Dad's answering machine, and Dad would always call back. He was good about that.

Melissa called him every once in a while just to talk. But I only called when I had a specific reason—like to find out what time he was picking us up for dinner, or to tell him UPS had delivered a package for him at the house. Even so, I knew I could reach him if I needed him. I thought about Brad Martin, a kid at school whose parents split up just before his father took a job with a shipping company in Singapore. *At least if Dad's gone,* I encouraged myself, *He's not gone far.*

In fact, if you added up the hours I spent in Dad's company—between one or two evenings out a week, a couple of T-ball games, and some of the weekend time—it probably wasn't much less than it had been before he moved out. At least that's what I told myself when I missed him. And I missed him every day.

I don't think I really understood what it was that I missed until the first weekend Mark and I stayed with Dad in his apartment. Mark was already sacked out in his sleeping bag back on the floor of the second bedroom. Dad went to take a shower and I sprawled out on his second-hand couch watching an old "M*A*S*H" rerun on a nine-inch portable black-and-white TV that rested on a card table in the corner of the living room. Hawkeye was in the middle of chest surgery with the operating room lights flickering on and off when I heard Dad back in the bathroom, gargling with mouthwash.

I suddenly realized I hadn't heard that familiar sound for over two months. Before that, I'd probably heard it every day of my life. And that's when it hit me why I missed Dad so much. It wasn't the big things like time and distance that had separated us. It was the little things. Like the sound of gargling; the rustling of the newspaper from the easy chair in the family room; the old familiar basketball shoes sitting in the corner on the back porch, always ready for an impromptu ten-minute workout in the driveway while Mom finished fixing supper; the smell of his after-shave lingering in the bathroom every morning after he'd gone.

There were dozens of little things. None significant by themselves. But when you add them together and subtract them all at once, they leave a giant hole in your life. Sitting alone in Dad's living room, the truth began to sink in. My own father was no longer a part of my everyday life—and I wasn't a part of his. There could never be enough weekly dinners out, there could never be enough weekend visits, to plug the hole.

Dad emerged from the bathroom a couple of minutes later wearing the navy terry cloth bathrobe I'd given him for Christmas a couple of years before. And I realized I hadn't seen him in that for over two months either.

As the credits rolled up at the end of the "M*A*S*H" episode, Dad walked to the card table and picked up a *TV Guide*. "There's an old Bogart movie on, and the Cubs are playing a late night game against the Padres. You're the guest, you choose."

I didn't want to be a guest in my own father's home. "I don't care. Either one."

"OK," he said, turning the channel selector. "Let's watch the ball game. It'll be easier to talk."

But there wasn't much to say. At least not much I felt like saying. So by the top of the fifth inning, with the score tied at one, I said, "It's getting late, Dad. I think I'll head on in to bed."

"A couple of times I thought you'd already zonked out on me. I don't think you've said anything for the last two innings."

"Guess I'm just not feeling very talkative tonight," I said. But I didn't tell him why.

Lying in my sleeping bag on the floor next to Mark, I couldn't sleep. I thought some more about the little things I'd missed since Dad moved out. I finally heard Dad shut off the TV and walk quietly down the hall to his room. And I began to think seriously for the first time what it would be like to live with Dad, in his apartment. Just the two of us, eating breakfast together in the morning. I wouldn't even mind fixing supper for him most nights. We'd have time to talk. We could decide to do things on a moment's notice instead of having to plan everything a week in advance.

I felt certain he'd let me if I wanted to. And I knew Mom wouldn't stop me if that was my choice. But the moment I thought about Mom, I realized it wasn't that easy. So far I'd been a passive observer of the painful rift between my parents. If I'd leaned toward any side, it was Mom's; Dad was the one who'd left. So asking to live with Dad could be seen as picking sides. And I didn't want to do that. I didn't want anything I did to hurt her any more than she'd been hurt already.

And yet, in realizing why I missed Dad so much, I finally understood that I couldn't regain the relationship I'd always had with my father without sharing his everyday life and having him share mine. If I lived with him, we'd have that.

But then I'd lose the relationship with Mom. And there'd be a hole there. And things would be different with Melissa and Mark. And . . . the only good solution, was having Dad come home. Then, and only then, we could be a real family again. It would happen. It had to. Because if it didn't, I'd have to choose. . . .

Lying there in the darkness, I prayed again. But I no longer cared about why it had all happened. I only wanted my parents together again. "God," I prayed. "Help Dad understand what this is doing to all of us.

Bring him home again!" Two miles wasn't very far. But in the quiet of Dad's apartment, I hoped it wasn't too far.

The one bright spot in my summer was Jennifer. I could hardly believe that with all the trauma in my family, that another part of my life could seem so great.

We'd go out at least once a week, usually twice. And we'd talk on the phone a lot of other nights. I'd never felt so comfortable with a girl before. Unlike some girls I'd known, she didn't ever make me feel like I had to impress her.

She had a book called *Creative Dates for Cheapskates* and after we'd been out a few times doing the usual date-type things, she suggested we try some of the ideas in the book. It made for some very unusual and very funny dates. Like the time we went to the airport to people-watch and we tried to guess people's occupations and destinations by their appearance. Once we even tried to confirm our guesses. I noticed a pudgy, balding man in a dark blue suit and guessed he was an undertaker on his way to Cleveland. Jennifer insisted he was a college professor on his way home to New York.

"Whoever's closest wins a free Coke from the loser, OK?" Jenifer proposed.

"OK, but how . . . ?"

"Just watch," Jennifer said, pulling a small notepad from her purse and walking toward the man as he stood looking at a monitor showing arriving and departing flights. I saw her saying something to the man and he nodded and replied. She wrote a short note on her pad, thanked him, and headed back toward me.

"Let's go," she said, taking my arm and heading me in the opposite direction. "Try to look official."

"Why? What did you tell him?"

She grinned. "The truth of course."

"What?"

"That I was taking a survey and wanted to ask him two simple questions. I needed to know his occupation and his destination this evening."

"What did he say?"

"He said he wasn't going anywhere, he'd just come to the airport to pick up his mother who was flying in from Phoenix."

"OK. So what's he do for a living?"

"He's a plumber."

When we finally quit laughing, I said, "Guess you owe me a Coke then."

"How do you figure that?" she wanted to know. "You think a plumber is closer to an undertaker than to a college professor?"

"No," I said. "But Cleveland is closer to Phoenix than New York is."

"But he wasn't going to Phoenix. He is staying right here."

"Well then, here is closer to Cleveland than it is to New York. You still owe me a Coke. A very large Coke. I'm thirsty."

"OK, OK," she conceded with a laugh. "But I'm beginning to believe your father was right about you. You are a real miser."

"Hey, when you're right, you're right."

"Or in this case, when you're wrong, you're right."

I grinned and shrugged. "Whatever."

Jennifer and I spent so much time together that Mom didn't bother to ask who I was talking to on the phone or who I was going out with on Friday nights. I don't know exactly when it started, but our families and friends seemed to consider us a couple. I know Mom liked Jennifer a lot; she said so. Melissa didn't say much, but she acted very friendly whenever Jennifer came over to watch TV or just play games with the family. And Mark adored her so much it was funny to watch him sit down beside her and try to tell her about all the great things he'd done that day.

Jennifer seemed to enjoy being around my family. More than I liked being around hers. Mrs. Heinz was always polite enough, but she was also cool. And she certainly didn't go out of her way to make me feel welcome. The first time Jennifer asked her if it'd be all right for me to stay for supper, she shrugged and said, "I guess so."

I ate there three times during the summer. But each meal felt awkward. Jennifer's twelve-year-old sister Valerie acted painfully shy, speaking only when directly questioned and then venturing only a few words. She hardly even looked at me, at least when I was looking.

My first time for supper, Mrs. Heinz asked me a few questions about myself, my family, and my plans after high school. But that seemed to be about the limit of her interest. After that she seemed at a total loss for conversational ideas. It amazed me that Jennifer was related to either of them.

The first evening Jennifer and I stayed at her house to watch a movie on the VCR, her mom kept peeking into the den every five or ten minutes all evening. I felt like I was under police surveillance. And all we were doing was sitting on the couch watching a movie.

Evidently her mom's behavior bothered Jennifer as much as it did me. Because when it was time for me to go, she walked me out to the car. "I'm sorry about

Mom," she said. "She takes a little getting used to."

"I don't think she trusts me," I said.

"It's nothing personal. She doesn't trust any man."

"Really?"

"I've heard her say it many times. After Dad left, especially after he moved to Texas and got remarried, she used to lecture us all the time: 'Never trust men. You gotta watch out. All they want from you is one thing. And once they get it they start looking to get it somewhere else. You can never trust them.'"

"Pretty cynical."

"I love her because she's my mom," explained Jennifer. "But she's a very bitter woman."

One night, the week after Mom and Dad's anniversary (which went uncelebrated), Jennifer and I stopped back by my house to pick up some concert tickets I'd left on the chest in my room. Everyone was gone (on a walk I found out later).

Jennifer headed for the family room while I ran upstairs. When I came back down she was standing beside the dining room table, looking at something. As I walked up behind her I saw the photo albums spread over the tabletop.

"Somebody was looking at some old photos," she said. "This album was open."

My parents' wedding album. There was a picture of my mom kissing my dad. And opposite that a shot of them facing each other and smiling. You could see the love on their faces and in the way their eyes seemed to connect.

"Mom must have gotten the pictures out. Last Friday was their anniversary," I said.

"Which one?"

"What?"

"Which anniversary? How many years?"

"Twenty." I turned to the front of the album to show her the date.

"Wow, Friday must have been a rough day for your mom."

"I guess so." I suddenly wished I'd done something for Mom. Or more accurately, I wished there was something I could have done. I still couldn't think of anything that would have been appropriate.

"Hey, Matt, here's your baby book!" Jennifer exclaimed, picking up another album. "Look at you. What a cutie!" She began thumbing through the pages. When she got to the obligatory shot of me as a two-year-old standing naked in the bathtub, I quickly turned the page. And she laughed. "I never understood why every parent in the world takes a photo like that. Or why they keep them," she said smiling.

"Blackmail, I suspect," I said.

"What's in the other albums?" Jennifer asked when we finished that one.

"Vacations. Family reunions. You name it."

She thumbed through a couple more exclaiming with laughter over shots of me as a kindergartner and again as an incredibly skinny twelve-year-old. "Your dad's in a lot more of the photos than your mom is. Why's that?"

"I hadn't noticed. I guess it's because Mom always had the camera. Dad was always too busy doing stuff with us to take pictures. So Mom became the family photographer who documented all our adventures."

"I think that's great," Jennifer said. "I wish my family had taken more pictures. They can bring back a lot of happy memories."

"Yeah," I agreed. But I thought to myself that they

were also sad reminders of what you've lost. "I remember going through some family pictures my mother's parents had," Jennifer said. "I found one shot of a family Christmas from the time I was six or seven. All my aunts and uncles and cousins were in it. And my father's picture had been cut right out of it."

"You're kidding!"

"No. It was like he'd been exorcised from the family."

Suddenly I felt very glad for all the pictures Mom had taken. And I felt very grateful in the knowledge that no one in our family would ever try to erase any of the good memories, let alone an individual. I couldn't imagine that kind of bitterness and resentment.

At least not then.

CHAPTER

6

I was pulled from a deep sleep on a mid-August night by the touch of a hand on my shoulder. I jerked suddenly to a sitting position and looked around. There was Mark, standing in the dark beside my bed, whimpering and crying. The LED display on my clock glowed at 1:17 A.M.

I shook my head a couple of times to clear the cobwebs of grogginess, then asked, "What's wrong?"

Mark stopped crying long enough to sputter, "I'm scared!"

"Did you have a bad dream?" His silhouette nodded.

"What are you afraid of?"

"Tigers and ghost and monsters," he said.

"Well, I haven't seen any of those things around here for a long time. I think you'll be safe if you just go back to bed."

"I had a bad dream."

"Do you want to talk about it?" I asked.

He shook his head. "Can I sleep with you?"

"I guess so," I said. "If you'll promise to be quiet and go back to sleep." I was sure if I sent him back to his own room he'd be back in ten minutes or he'd go wake up Mom or Melissa. So I rolled over to make room.

He'd no sooner settled down than he sat up again. "Matt?"

"Hmmm."

"Matt?"

"Lie down, Mark. Go to sleep."

"Do you snore like Dad, Matt?"

"No," I answered, smiling in the dark because I knew what he was thinking. "But I'm sure you will be safe from any wild animals if you'll just lie still and be very quiet." Sometimes when we'd go camping Dad would snore so loud he'd wake us all up. But when we complained he insisted fathers had deliberately learned to snore over the centuries as a means of protecting their wives and children by scaring off dangerous night creatures. It became a family joke—once we got old enough not to be scared of the dark anymore.

Mark eased back onto the pillow again. He remained still for all of fifteen seconds before he began twisting and turning in search of a more comfortable position.

"Would you please lie still and go to sleep!" I hissed at him.

"Are you awake, Matt?"

"No, I always talk in my sleep!" Realizing sarcasm is wasted on six-year-olds, I added, "Yeah, I'm awake. What's the matter?"

"I miss Dad. I wish he'd come home."

"I know, guy. Me, too."

After Mark finally drifted off to sleep, I was still wide awake. Listening to his regular, little-kid breathing I remembered being his age and waking up from nightmares. I'd pad quietly down the hall, tiptoe into Mom and Dad's room and crawl into bed between the two of them. Usually they wouldn't even wake up, but Dad would put his arm around me, and I'd feel so warm and safe that I'd go back to sleep in no time. Sometime during the night Dad must have carried me back to my own room, because I'd always awaken the next morning, tightly tucked under the covers of my own bed.

The memory filled me with a sudden sadness. Even more for Mark than for myself, because Dad wasn't there for him now when he woke up scared. So I turned on my side, put an arm over my little brother, and pulled him close to share what warmth I could.

Maybe it was the natural result of sleeping with a restless six-year-old, or maybe my subconscious was triggered by the thought of nightmares. Whatever the reason, I had one.

It started out as a replay of a traumatic childhood memory. I'd been about ten when it had happened. Dad and I had been wading down a small river, fishing. We both wore fishermen's waders; mine, though the smallest size Dad could find, were bulky and awkward to walk in. Dad had waded ahead of me, feeling for good footing and pointing out where to fish. "Move out toward the middle a little," he'd called. "It's shallow right there. And you can cast over by those tree stumps along the other side."

I still couldn't quite cast to the stumps from the middle of the river, so I had waded a little farther out. One second I was walking on a solid bottom and the next step I dropped right off a ledge into deep water. My head went under and I kicked to the surface.

Immediately water had begun to fill my waders, and I was pulled back under as the current dragged me downstream. I had panicked, kicking and thrashing and rolling in the water. Then my feet had touched bottom, and I shoved off desperately toward the surface. When my face broke into the air, there was my dad standing in chest-deep water. His hand had clamped me by the shirt, and he had dragged me, spitting and coughing, back to the shore.

The nightmare was worse. The water closed over my head, and I felt myself being swept downstream. When I hit bottom I shoved upwards with all my strength. But when I broke the surface, no one was there. I began to sink again as the current swept me helplessly down the river. The third time I came up to catch a breath I grabbed onto a log, but the current swept me on toward a thundering waterfall higher than Niagara. I tried to kick the log toward shore, but my legs felt like lead, and the rushing current carried me over the brink of the falls where I tumbled down, down, down. . . .

I woke in a sweat, my arm clamped around Mark. I rolled onto my back, and as I waited for my heart to quit pounding, I thought about the dream. You didn't have to be Sigmund Freud to interpret this one. Dad had always been there when I needed him before. Now he was gone. For me as well as for Mark.

The next night Jennifer and I had a date. But I wasn't exactly scintillating company. "Guess I must seem boring tonight," Jennifer said as I drove her home.

"Oh, no," I said, trying to recall some reason for her irritated tone. "Why do you say that?"

She grinned and I realized she was teasing. "You just yawned for the umpteenth time tonight," she said.

"Sorry. I didn't sleep much last night."

"It's OK. I could tell you were tired."

"Yeah, Mark came and got in my bed because he couldn't sleep." Jennifer laughed when I told her about the snoring bit. She got quiet though when I told her about him missing Dad and wishing he'd come home. I didn't say anything about my own nightmare.

"Separation and divorce can be especially hard on little kids," she said. "On the one hand they are so into themselves and their own little lives that they seem to adjust faster than anyone else. But they understand less and can have a hard time actually realizing what's happening."

"You sound like a shrink," I said.

"Sorry," Jennifer replied. "I did a lot of reading on the subject. For three years after my parents broke up, my little sister Valerie made the same wish when she'd blow out her birthday candles. 'What did ya wish for, Val?' we'd ask. 'I wished that Daddy would come back,' she'd say, and the party would be very quiet for a while because everyone else knew it could never happen. We finally quit asking her about her wish."

I thought about what she said for a few seconds before I responded. "Well, I don't think it's time for Mark to quit wishing yet. I'm not ready to give up hope yet either."

"I know," Jennifer said. "I'm sorry. I didn't mean to imply you should."

"It's OK," I assured her. "I know I have to face the possibility that my parents might actually get a divorce." It was the first time I'd ever admitted the possibility out loud. And there was no comfort in the words.

Perhaps it was that conversation with Jennifer. Or Mark's fears. Or my own nightmare. Or maybe it was the combination of all those things. But over the next couple of days I became convinced that I needed to have a heart-to-heart talk with Dad. I didn't know what I would say, or what I could say, but he needed to know what this separation was doing to the family. To Mark, to Melissa, to Mom, and to me. If he only knew . . . . I called Dad late one night.

"I'd like to talk with you when you've got some time," I told him.

"Now's fine if you want," he said.

"No, I want to come by and see you."

"OK," Dad said. "Any time. Tomorrow night?"

"Sounds good," I said, thinking it would give me a day to decide what I was going to say.

"I should be home about six. If I'm not here, I'll be here soon. Just let yourself in. You still have the key I gave you when you and Mark stayed over?"

"Yeah, Dad. No problem. See you tomorrow night."

But I still wasn't sure what I'd say when I locked my ten-speed into the rack outside Dad's apartment the next evening. I'd considered starting by asking his plans, to see how he felt about coming home. But depending on his answer, that might make it more awkward to say what I wanted to say. I didn't want him to feel guilty. And I knew I couldn't force him to come home; I wouldn't have wanted to. But I wanted him to know the truth about what was happening so he could make an informed decision. I knew facts and feelings were all jumbled together, and I didn't want to get all emotional. Yet I wanted him to know how I felt.

It was all very complicated and I was halfway tempted to go home and forget it. But I'd already done too good a job of convincing myself this was something I had to do. Whether it did any good or not, I had to try. It might just work.

Dad's car wasn't in the lot so I went ahead and used the key to get past the security door and then into his apartment. I flicked on the TV to see what was on while I waited. Just news. So I walked idly around the apartment.

He hadn't done much with it. The walls were bare. So were the windows, though it didn't matter much with a second floor apartment. Dad had picked up a dinette set at a garage sale—a small table and only three chairs. The couch and the card table with the TV were it for living room furniture, unless you counted the boxes of books stacked along the wall. The second bedroom had more boxes of books. And then there was Dad's bedroom. In one corner stood the lamp and the old recliner he'd taken from his office at home. He didn't have an actual bed, just a mattress sitting on a plywood platform set up on cement blocks. His clothes were hanging up or folded on shelves in his walk-in closet—though a couple of pairs of pants, some shirts, and a rumpled sports jacket were lying in the recliner.

Walking around the apartment I realized Dad was living in a different world from the rest of the family now. Everything looked so casual, so simple. He obviously didn't have much, but then maybe he didn't need much.

I began to imagine again what it would be like to live there with him. To share his life-style. But as appealing as it was to think about being with him every day, I couldn't help thinking about Mom and Melissa and Mark. Without me. And I considered telling him how I felt—wanting to live with him, but not wanting to leave home. Surely he could understand that conflict.

I looked around restlessly. Where was he? It was almost 6:30. I walked back into the kitchen and noticed the answering machine on the counter. The light indicated it was on. *If he got held up at the office, he might have called to leave me a message,* I reasoned.

I rewound the tape and punched the play button. The first message was from Mark saying Mom was taking him and Melissa to the mall shopping and he'd call again when they got back. Probably about eight. Then there was a call from an insurance agent who said he'd call back. And a guy who used to work with Dad called to leave a number.

Then there was a woman's voice.

"Hi, Ben. I'll call again later tonight. My flight didn't get in until late this afternoon." She didn't give her name. Her voice sounded silky, her tone familiar. "I wanted you to know I was back in town." *Real familiar.* She started talking faster to beat the thirty-second timer on the tape. "One more thing. Hope you don't mind, but I picked up a set of curtains for you. I'm not going to stay over one more night in that apartment until you get something on those bedroom windows. I'll call later. I missed you." Click.

It was the last message on the tape. I wouldn't have heard anything else anyway.

It's gotta be some mistake, I thought numbly. *A practical joke. A wrong number.* But even as I tried to think of some believable explanation, I knew the truth. Even if I couldn't believe it.

I bolted for the door without stopping to shut off the tape. I didn't want to be there when Dad got home. I couldn't face him. Not then. *Maybe never!* I told myself as I unlocked my bike and headed out of the complex by a back way to avoid meeting him on the street.

Mom and the other kids were still at the mall when I got home. That was good. I didn't feel like facing them either. I was absolutely certain that Mom didn't know Dad was seeing anyone else. *So why did I have to know?*

I parked my bike in the garage and kicked the basketball out into the yard. Then I walked out after it.

I'd lowered the backboard so Mark could shoot some the day before. The rim was only about nine feet high. So when I picked up the ball and turned toward the goal, I didn't even think. I just took a couple of dribbles, leaped, and slammed the ball down through the hoop. The violence of the act felt good. So I grabbed the ball and drove again. Harder! Again. Harder. The fourth time my foot slipped as I was taking off and I instinctively grabbed the rim to regain my balance as the ball ricocheted off. Before I could let go I heard a loud snap from where the rim was bolted to the board. I retrieved the ball and drove again. I slammed the ball through and the rim bent down five degrees. Again I slammed the ball through the hoop, harder this time, banging my arm against the iron in the process. The rim bent further and I could see a crack on the backboard itself, right where the goal was bolted on. One more time I leaped and slammed the ball and the board cracked as the rim bent down and broke off, crashing to the driveway with a small chunk of the backboard still bolted on.

Then I tossed the ball and the broken rim out onto the grass and headed inside to my room. I turned on the radio and scanned the dial till I found a station playing hard rock, and I cranked up the volume as loud as it would go.

CHAPTER

7

Mom asked me about the rim the next morning before I took off for work. "I slam-dunked one last night and it broke right off," I said.

"I guess that backboard has taken a lot of strain over the years," she said, accepting the explanation.

"Guess so."

"Oh, your Dad called a few minutes ago while you were in the shower. Said he was sorry he missed you last night. Didn't you go over there last night?"

"Something came up."

"He wanted you to call."

"Later," I said, grabbing a hot bagel from the toaster and spreading it with cream cheese. "I gotta go to work."

I drove over to Jennifer's that night, and we sat on the front porch in the swing. She rested her head on my shoulder as we swung in silence for a few minutes.

"You're a talkative one tonight," she finally said. I didn't want to tell her. I knew talking about it would make it seem that much more real. I resented even knowing about it myself. But I'd been able to think of nothing else all day. I had to tell someone.

So I explained how I'd gone to talk to Dad to let him know how I was feeling. I recounted my arrival, the wait in his apartment. How I walked around, and then how I decided to check the answering machine. I told her about the sexy voice and what was said.

As I talked, Jennifer slipped her hand into mine and when I finished she lifted her head and looked into my face. "I'm sorry, Matt. That must have been very painful for you."

I nodded. "You don't act surprised."

"I guess I'm not."

"You don't know my dad."

"I'm sorry, Matt."

"Your mom isn't right you know. Not every man is like that. My dad isn't like that."

"It must have been even rougher facing your father."

"I didn't. I split before he got there. I went home and ripped the rim right off my backboard."

"Is that how you hurt your arm?" She lightly traced her forefinger over an ugly bruise on the underside of my right wrist.

"Yeah," I admitted. "It was really dumb. But I was so angry I felt like destroying something."

"I don't blame you," Jennifer said as she lifted my arm and gently kissed the discoloration above the wrist.

I was content to sit in silence again for a time. When I was ready to talk again, Jennifer seemed to sense it. "What are you going to say to your father?" she asked.

I'd been asking myself the same question all day. "I don't know. Right now I don't want to face him at all. He phoned this morning, but I didn't return the call."

When I got home from Jennifer's that night, Mom told me Dad had called again. I told her I'd call later and went up to my room to bed. Next morning, when I got downstairs, Mom said he'd called again before I'd gotten up. "He sounded anxious to talk to you. Said to call him at his office when you got up."

"Gotta go now," I said, giving Mom a quick peck on the cheek and heading for the door. "I'll have to call him from work."

But I didn't. I knew I had to talk to him sooner or later. But later sounded better until I figured out what to say—or even if I should say anything—about what I'd heard.

I was updating the inventory on electrical supplies, concentrating on the monitor screen in the stockroom of the hardware store when I felt a tap on my shoulder. When I looked up and saw Dad, my heart sank. But I forced a smile, "Hey, what brings you down here?"

"You're a hard guy to get a hold of," he said. "But I figured you had to eat lunch sometime, right?"

I glanced at my watch: ten to twelve. "Sure. Sounds good," I said. Hopefully with more conviction than I felt.

We drove to a nearby deli, ordered sandwiches and soft drinks, and took them back to the car. We left the doors open to let the breeze blow through.

"Sorry I missed you at the apartment the other night," Dad said after a couple bites of his corned beef sandwich.

"It's OK," I said. "Something came up."

He chewed for a minute, swallowed, and turned to me. "I think I know what came up, Matt." *He knew?* "If you're the one who checked my answering machine, that is."

Of course, he knew. I didn't rewind the tape. I nodded. "When you were late, I thought maybe you'd called and left a message for me."

"So you heard . . . ?"

I nodded again.

"I'm sorry you had to learn like that. I was going to tell you before long. When the time was right. When I had the time to explain—"

"It didn't sound like there was much to explain," I cut him off, bitterness encasing my words.

"You're wrong, Matt. I want you to understand. I want you to listen."

When I didn't say anything he went on. "I never wanted to hurt you, or Melissa, or Mark. Or even your mom. Especially your mom. I still love your mom very much. You may not believe it, but I do.

"I didn't intend for any of this to happen. But it did. It just happened. I met Gwynn when her firm did some legal work for my company."

Her name was Gwynn; the name fit the voice.

"She's a lawyer. We had lunch a couple of times; strictly business. She told me she was interested in backpacking and had been looking to buy some new equipment. I told her I could work a discount if she wanted to get something from my company. She placed an order, and when it came in I gave her a call. She said she'd have to get it a couple of days later because her car was in the shop and she was working at home. I volunteered to drop it by her condo after work and . . ."

I didn't want to hear any more of this. I didn't want to know about my father and this woman named Gwynn. But I wanted so desperately to understand that I had to listen.

"She asked me to stay for supper. Said it was the least she could do to thank me for being so nice. I turned down the invitation. Said, 'Some other time maybe.' She called me the next week and asked, 'How about that dinner I owe you?'

"It was during spring break. You kids and your mom were gone out to Aunt Ruth's for a couple of days. So I agreed and. . . ."

Spring break? That was back in March. Before . . . , I looked at him. "You started seeing this . . . this woman in March?" I asked.

Dad nodded. "Yes, but we were just friends. We had that dinner. And the next week we had lunch. And another dinner. And then a couple of lunches. We just enjoyed each other's company. We laughed. We talked.

"Your mother and I haven't been communicating all that much the last few years. It's probably my fault. I didn't plan for any of this to happen. Everything just suddenly mushroomed. I'm sorry to be putting you through this. I still love you all. God knows I didn't plan to hurt any of you."

Right! I thought angrily. *God knows. But if God knows, then how could you do this? Why couldn't he stop you?* But all I said out loud was, "I gotta get back to work."

Back at the store I sat in the stockroom staring at the computer for ten minutes without seeing a thing. Finally I got up and went to find Mr. Hagstrom. "I think I'm gonna go home," I told him. "I'm not feeling too good this afternoon."

"Go on then," he said. "Take care of yourself and we'll see you tomorrow."

No one was home when I got there, so I went straight to my room. Lying across the bed in front of the air-conditioning vent, I tried to absorb everything Dad had said. Up until then I'd been angry, but at a situation I didn't understand. I'd been angry that my parents weren't getting along, that Dad was living in his apartment, that our family was torn apart. But the anger hadn't been focused because it's hard to be angry at a situation.

Now I was angrier than ever, and not at some nebulous situation—but at Dad. I'd had no one to blame before. Now I knew exactly who to blame.

I was angry at him for hurting Mom. For hurting Melissa and Mark. And me. I was angry at him because I'd always admired him and he'd betrayed my respect. I was angry for all the things he'd taught us growing up, all the things he said he believed about the importance of family and how God honors a Christian marriage. I was angry at him for being such a great example of a husband and father for all those years, only to dump it all now. I was angry that he'd taught me to believe in a value system that he himself had given up for some sexy-sounding lady lawyer who came on to him over a business lunch. I was angry at him for being my father.

When I couldn't think of any more reasons to be angry at Dad, I even got angry at Mom. For being such an organized person. For not being more spontaneous. For not being more . . . attractive to Dad. But that wasn't fair. She wasn't the one who'd changed. She wasn't the one who'd had an . . . an affair. Dad was. He was the one who deserved the anger.

And God. I was angry at him because he hadn't stopped it. He hadn't made Dad strong enough to stand up to temptation. He hadn't cared enough to hold a loving Christian family together. What good was our faith if it couldn't do that? For that matter, what good was any faith if the man who did more than anyone else to teach you about it could walk away from it, and from his family, on a moment's notice?

But mostly I was angry at Dad. And because I still loved him, the anger was tearing me up inside.

It was hard to feel what I felt and to keep it all bottled up inside. My last week on my summer job I kept to myself and was unusually quiet. At home I holed up in my room. Whenever I could I went over to Jennifer's. She was the one person who kept me from exploding inside.

I told her how angry I felt. She listened. She told me she thought the feelings I had sounded understandable given the circumstances. But I wasn't so sure. She couldn't feel the intensity of the anger inside me. I didn't think she understood how much that anger scared me. But she listened. And she loved me. And I didn't think I'd be able to take it without her.

The only other person who could break through the anger those next few days was Mark. Mom was out late to some church meeting one night and asked me to baby-sit and put him to bed. Before he climbed into his bunk, he got down on his knees and prayed, thanking God for the beautiful day and asking God to bless everyone he loved. Then he closed his prayer by saying, "And please, dear Lord, make tomorrow be the day that Daddy comes home and we all get to be a family again."

After I tucked him in and kissed him goodnight, I went to my own room, shut the door, and cried—really cried for the first time since the day Dad had said he was leaving. And I was still angry. Because I knew God wasn't going to answer Mark's prayer, tomorrow or ever.

I couldn't decide which was worse, being a six-year-old with naive, eternal hope or being seventeen and knowing there was no hope at all.

CHANGE

Jennifer leaned her head against the back of the park bench where we were sitting and stared dreamily up through the trees overhead. Her eyes seemed to reflect the blue of the brilliant afternoon sky. Or maybe it was the other way around and it was the afternoon sky that reflected the brilliant blue of her eyes. *I'm in love. No doubt about it.*

"I can't believe summer is almost over," she said. "And I really can't believe my last year of high school starts next week."

I watched her eyes close. She looked so peaceful. After a few seconds, her eyes opened again, and she turned her head toward me. "Have you noticed how, the older you get, the faster time seems to fly?"

I grinned. "Maybe that's because you're having that much more fun now. Especially since you met me."

"No. Seriously."

I feigned a frown. "I was serious. Now I'm hurt."

She laughed. "You look pitiful when you're hurt." I

frowned harder, but she ignored me and went on. "Remember how long a week, a day, even an hour seemed when you were a little kid? Now a whole summer flashes by in an instant."

It did seem like yesterday, not three months before, that I'd first asked her out. "Which only proves what I was saying," I insisted with a smile. "You met me just before the start of the summer."

She rolled her eyes and shook her head. "On the one hand, a whole summer or even a whole four years of high school can fly by. On the other hand, a particular day, a particular hour can seem to last forever. Especially the bad days, or the bad hours." She closed her eyes in thought again. "Maybe time is all relative."

I thought about the eternity that had passed in the three months since Dad had told us he was moving out. After a time I broke the silence by observing: "You must be feeling philosophical today."

Jennifer opened her eyes and looked at me again. "Maybe so. But can you believe that you're starting your senior year in high school next week?"

"I hadn't thought that much about it," I said. "At least not until this week when I got a copy of my official class schedule in the mail along with a notice of my lab fees and the price of my books. Mom almost choked when she saw the total charges. She said the back-to-school supplies and expenses for the three of us were going to shoot the family budget."

"My mom always says August is a tougher month financially than December," Jennifer said.

"That makes sense," I said. "I just never thought about all the costs of going back to school. Guess I never had to think about it. We were never rich, but

Dad's a successful salesman and we've always had what we needed."

Jennifer was staring into the sky again. "It doesn't really matter how much money is coming in. When you divide it over two households there can't be as much to go around."

"I guess you're right," I said. "I just hadn't thought about it that way."

"I've had to think about it," Jennifer said. "It was tough enough for our family right after my parents' divorce, when my father was paying his child support on a regular basis. But since he moved to Texas and only sends a check once in a while, my mom really has to stretch to pay the bills some months. It's hard. In fact, it's one of the things I resent about the divorce.

"Mom's always apologizing for not being able to buy me as many things as she'd like. But I know it's not her fault. So I try to pay for most of my own clothes with the money I make from baby-sitting and from any jobs I get during the summer. I'm glad to do what I can to help take some of the financial pressure off Mom. But when I stop and realize I don't have anything saved toward college, it's hard not to feel bitter about the whole situation."

As we walked back to Jennifer's house from the park that Sunday afternoon I couldn't help thinking about the $4700 I had in the bank. My parents had started a college savings account for me when I was in elementary school; but most of what was in there now I'd earned working part-time and summers the last couple of years.

Despite my conversation with Jennifer, Mom's big decision a few days later still surprised me. But at least

I understood what she was thinking. And why.

She was sitting at the kitchen table when I walked in after school, the third day of classes. "Sit down, Matt," she said. "I've got something I want to talk to you about.

"Want a snack?" she asked as I pulled out a chair. "I baked some chocolate chocolate-chip cookies this afternoon. They're still warm."

"Sure. I knew I smelled something chocolate." When I was little, Mom always used to have a snack ready when I got home from school. She'd sit down at the table with me and go over any papers I'd bring home. She still followed the routine with Mark.

"I wanted to talk with you before the younger kids got home," Mom said, setting a plate of cookies in front of me and pouring a tall plastic tumbler of milk. She sat down.

"You know money has been pretty tight lately," she said. "Your dad has been giving us all he can. But it's just not enough. Especially with school expenses now. And our utilities will go up as the weather gets colder."

"We'll be OK, Mom," I assured her. "I could start paying room and board from the money I earn on Saturdays at the hardware store. And there's my savings money. I don't need that right now."

She shook her head. "No. You'll be needing your college savings soon enough. I've got a better solution. I'm going to work."

"Doing what?" I didn't mean it like it sounded. "I mean, what kind of job did you have in mind?"

"Actually, I've got a job already. I had the interview this morning, and they made me an offer on the spot." She smiled, looking a bit proud of the accomplishment.

I didn't know what to say and I guess it showed, because she grinned at me and said, "Don't look so surprised! I used to be a pretty good office manager before you came along. And while some of my old skills are a bit rusty, it's not as if I haven't been using my organizational abilities to keep this family running for the last seventeen years."

"Congratulations!" I finally said. "I'm not surprised you could get a job. I'm just surprised that you already did. Where?"

"At an insurance agency out near Grandma and Grandpa's. The office manager is quitting in three months to have a baby. So it'll give me time to learn the ropes. I start this coming Monday."

I could tell she was excited. "That's great, Mom," I said.

"There's only one problem." She looked up, and I met her gaze.

"What's that?" I asked.

"Office hours are eight to four-thirty. And it's a half-hour drive from here. I won't be able to be here when you kids take off for school or . . ."

"Don't worry, Mom. Melissa and I can handle breakfast, and I can make sure the kids get off OK before I leave."

Mom smiled and nodded. "But I'm more concerned about the afternoons. I won't be able to get home until at least five. And Mark gets home by a quarter after three. I think Melissa is still a little young to be in charge and you often have things going after school."

I shrugged. "The only thing that would keep me after school is the newspaper. And I was thinking about dropping out of that anyway."

"But you enjoyed working on the paper last year."

"Yeah," I admitted. "But all the top positions for this year went to people who've been on the paper for two years. Maybe if I'd been appointed as editor over a section, maybe Sports or even Feature Editor, I could get excited about it. But I'm only going to be a general reporter and I've already done that. I won't be missing out on much if I don't do it; I was thinking about talking to the advisor, Mr. Swiderski, and resigning anyway."

Mom looked skeptical. "You're not just saying that?"

"No, Mom. I mean it."

"Well," she conceded. "It would make things easier if you could be here most days. I might be able to find someone who does after school day-care. But we'd have to arrange transportation, and the cost would really eat into my income."

"No problem, Mom. I can do it," I insisted. It seemed the least I could do. Until I found Mr. Swiderski in the newspaper office at lunch the next day.

"Matt, hi! Glad you stopped by," he said. "I was going to look you up this week to talk to you about the newspaper staff."

I nodded. "That's what I wanted to talk to you about."

"Great! I've got what I hope is good news. Janet Davis and I have been talking about plans for this year. And she'd like to redefine her position as editor. She wants to concentrate on writing and editing the editorial page to give the paper a stronger editorial voice about campus issues. But she doesn't think she can do that and still supervise the rest of the paper. So we've created a new position we haven't had for a few years: Managing Editor. And we both think you'd do a good job."

"But I don't think . . ."

"Before you say anything, let me tell you what the position would involve." Mr. Swiderski went on to explain that the managing editor would coordinate all the sections of the paper and actually supervise the section editors, keep tabs on the week-by-week and day-to-day work of the paper, and—along with the editor and the advisor—make all final decisions regarding the content of the paper.

"That sounds like an interesting position," I told him when he finally finished with his sales pitch. *Interesting? It sounded fantastic.* So fantastic that my next words came very hard.

"But I came by to see you today to resign from the staff."

"Oh?" I could see the disappointment written on Mr. Swiderski's face. "Can I ask why?"

"My mother's going back to work, and I've told her I'd be home right after school every day to keep an eye on my little brother and sister."

He wasn't ready to give up. "Can you take the weekend to think about it? Maybe see if you can work something out?"

"I guess so." But I didn't see much point.

"It'd look good on your record going into college," he said. "I hope you can work something out."

He was right. It would look good. And it would be a fun challenge. But I didn't see any way to work it out.

I told Jennifer about the managing editor position when we went out that Friday night. "What did your Mom say?" she wanted to know.

"I haven't told her yet. I don't know if I should."

"Why not? I think she'd want to know."

"I know that," I admitted. "But it would just complicate things for her."

"Don't you want the position?" Jennifer asked.

"Sure, I want it. But I'm old enough to know I can't have everything I want."

"No one expects you to be a martyr. Your mom wouldn't want you to give up something you really care about."

"I know," I said. "But she's already giving up a lot to go back to work. It seems like the least I can do is help take care of Mark and Melissa."

I could tell Jennifer wanted to say more. But she let it drop. And we didn't talk about it any more that night.

On Monday I went into the newspaper office at school and told Mr. Swiderski I really would have liked the job, but I couldn't do it. And I decided not to tell Mom about the decision.

It seemed like the right thing to do at the time. But it wasn't easy. And it certainly didn't seem fair.

CHAPTER

9

For almost a month after I found out about Dad's girlfriend I pretty much avoided him. It wasn't too hard. Whenever he came by or scheduled something for us kids, I made sure I had other plans. During the week it was easy, I could always use homework as an excuse. And on weekends there was work, or I'd make a date with Jennifer.

But one late September Saturday afternoon, Mom called me to the phone. As she handed me the receiver she said, "It's your father."

"Hello?"

"Matt, I think it's time you and I talk," he said. "I'll be by in five minutes. We'll go get a Coke or something. Just you and me. For an hour or so. OK?"

I agreed reluctantly. There was no reasonable way out of it.

"How's ice cream sound?" he greeted me as I climbed into the front seat of his car. "I skipped lunch, and a double dip of Baskin-Robbins' sounds real good to me."

"Fine," I said. We drove the first few blocks in strained silence before he began asking about school, my classes, etc. I answered, but I didn't volunteer any information he didn't ask about directly. I felt as if I was making polite conversation with a stranger. I guess, in a way, he was a stranger. Because the father I'd known for seventeen years would never have done what he did. The father I'd known would have been stronger, would have held to his beliefs, would have died before he let anyone or anything hurt his family.

We pulled into the small shopping center parking lot and got out of the car. "What do you want?" Dad asked, as he pushed open the door and entered the Baskin-Robbins. Before I could answer, he said, "Don't tell me. I can guess. A double dip. One scoop of Jamocha Almond Fudge and one scoop of Rocky Road?"

No stranger could know me that well, and that bothered me. But then I knew exactly what he would order—and that bothered me, too.

Five minutes later we were sitting in the front seat of Dad's car with the windows rolled down. "You know," he said, "this is crazy. You're my son. I'm your father. We can't go on forever avoiding each other."

"I know that," I replied.

"I guess you're mad at me, huh?"

I focused on my ice cream cone. "I guess so."

"But you haven't told your mother." It was a statement. Yet the question was inferred: Why?

I turned and looked at him for the first time that day. "I didn't think I should be the one to tell her," I said.

Dad nodded. "You're right. I'm going to explain everything to her."

"When?"

"Before long. When I think she's ready to hear it."

I didn't think she'd ever be ready to hear what he had to say.

"In the meantime," Dad went on, "you and I can't go on like we have the past few weeks. It's not only hard on us, it's hard on everyone else in the family. Mark asked me this week why you never go out to eat with us anymore. They all think something's wrong."

"Something *is* wrong!" I said. "I can't pretend there isn't."

"I don't want you to pretend," he said. "I know I can't expect you not to be angry. And maybe we can't have the same relationship we had before; it hurts me to say that. I want it to be the same, but maybe it can't be. At least we can have some kind of relationship. I want to try, OK? Can we start over?"

Dad smiled when I said, "OK." What else could I say? I knew he was right. We couldn't go on like we had been. And yet how do you begin a new relationship after seventeen years of the old one? There's too much history and too much hurt to start from scratch. How can someone you know so well become a stranger? I was learning how terribly hard it was not knowing and not liking someone you love so much.

The change of routine at home was an easier adjustment. Mornings were more hectic than when Mom was there, especially when I got ambitious (or hungry) and fixed scrambled eggs, sausage, and toast. But most of the time we just had cold cereal or yogurt, or maybe something like bagels that I could pop into the toaster and have in a minute or so. Melissa was certainly old enough to get herself ready for school. And Mark did pretty well because Mom would set his clothes out the night before.

Afternoons were even less pressured since there wasn't any real time deadline. Melissa would do her homework right after school, and Mark would play in the backyard, watch something we taped off the Disney channel on cable, or sometimes go down the block to play with a friend. A lot of days Mom would leave instructions for getting supper started, but I didn't mind. Actually I didn't mind any of my new responsibilities. We all pitched in, and it gave us, at least it gave me, a satisfying sense of independence. I did feel a twinge of regret the day the first issue of the school paper came out, but it didn't last long. I simply accepted my new role at home and did what had to be done.

The changes seemed hardest on Mom. She came home almost every night so exhausted that she'd sit through supper in a semi-trance, occasionally complaining about the rush hour traffic and apologizing for being so tired. She'd usually get a second wind about the time she put Mark down, and then she'd want to talk about her day.

She'd laugh about some of the eccentric clients she'd had to deal with. She'd tell me about her boss and she'd even talk through some new office procedure she was thinking of implementing. One night she stopped right in the midst of recounting her day and said, "I don't mean to blab on and on. You've got more interesting things to think about."

"It's OK, Mom," I said. "It's nice to know what's going on with you and your job." And sometimes it was interesting to be able to picture Mom in an office, supervising three other people, soothing irate clients, etc. But mostly, I listened to her tell about the routine of her day because she seemed to need someone to talk to. And when she asked my opinion on something, I felt as if she was treating me like an adult. With that and the added responsibilities for the younger kids, I felt more like an adult than I ever had before.

After Mom's first six weeks on the job, her nightly recaps settled into a fairly predictable pattern. She evidently still needed to talk to help unwind. But there wasn't much new to say. Until one night the week before Halloween. The second she walked in I could see she'd been crying.

"Mom, are you OK?"

"I'll be fine," she insisted. And the next moment Mark burst into the kitchen to greet her with a kiss and show her a paper his teacher had returned with a big "Super Job" stamped in red at the top of the page.

"What's wrong?" I asked as Mark ran out to get something else he wanted her to see.

Suddenly Mark was back. Mom looked at me and said, "Maybe we can talk later," so I knew it wasn't something she wanted to say in front of Mark. I thought maybe Dad had finally told her about his girlfriend, or she'd somehow found out.

Melissa went to a friend's house after supper that night. After Mom put Mark to bed, she came downstairs and started putting things away in the kitchen. I went to get a can of pop out of the refrigerator and then sat at the kitchen table to drink it while Mom scrubbed furiously at the sink.

"What's wrong, Mom?"

She put down the can of Comet and the plastic

scrubber she had in her other hand and turned to face me. "It really shouldn't concern you, Matt."

Maybe it is about Dad.

"But I'm so upset I really have to talk to someone."

It has to be.

"It's about my boss."

"Mr. Basinger?" I felt relieved. Mostly.

"He had a long lunch with a client today. One of those three-martini lunches evidently. When he came back to the office with the client after two o'clock, he was talking and laughing a little too loudly. I think everyone in the office noticed. After the client left, Mr. Basinger buzzed my desk and asked me to bring him some forms. I took them in and put them on his desk, and as I turned to leave, he reached out and patted me on the bottom. I almost slapped him."

I looked at Mom and felt the anger building inside me—I wanted to punch the guy's lights out. "So what did you do?" I asked, keeping my voice calm.

"Nothing, I'm afraid," Mom said. "I guess I was too surprised. I just kept on walking out of his office. I was so steamed that I almost walked right out of the building and came home. But as I sat at my desk I realized he'd never done anything like that before, and I figured it was probably because he'd had too much to drink at lunch. So I decided to ignore the whole thing and hope it never happened again.

"Just before closing time, he called me into his office again. I made sure to leave the door open just in case. But he politely asked me to take a seat. The booze seemed to have worn off and I figured he was going to apologize for the earlier incident.

"Instead, he talked about what a good job I've been

doing. What a fine contribution I was making to the office. How he was glad he'd hired me and so on. He went on and on. And I figured he was building up to an apology. But he kept on talking until I heard the front door of the office close, and I knew everyone else had gone.

"He heard it, too. Because he said, 'I guess it's time to head home. But before you go, there's one thing I'd like to say.' Then he told me he has a weekend convention in New York next month, and he wondered if I'd go with him. I hoped he only had business on his mind, but I told him I wouldn't be able to go, that I had family responsibilities. He said it was OK, that he understood. But as I started to leave, he asked me if I'd at least have dinner with him Friday night. And I just happen to know his wife is gone this week, visiting her sister out in Colorado."

I couldn't believe what I was hearing. "What did you say to him?"

"I just told him 'no' and left. I didn't get really upset until I started driving home. I kept telling myself it was just the booze. That this was just a onetime thing. I'm not exactly used to having a married man make a pass at me."

I knew how she felt. I wasn't exactly used to hearing my mom talk about someone making a pass at her.

Mom continued, "The more I thought about it, the more upset I got. I'm not about to put up with that kind of thing. But I like my job, and I like the other people who work in the office. I thought I was doing a good job, but suddenly I'm not even sure of that. I have to wonder if all the positive feedback I was getting from Mr. Basinger was really on the level. For that matter, I told him your father and I were separated when I went in for the job interview. Maybe that's the only reason he hired me; the only reason he's kept me on."

She was getting upset again. Tears had begun to run down her cheeks as she talked.

I wanted desperately to reassure her. "But Mom, the other people in the office think you're doing a good job. You've had nothing but positive responses from them."

Mom nodded. "You're right. But in a way, that makes this worse. Until today I liked my job. I don't want to leave. But I don't know what to do. Part of me wants to believe what happened today will never happen again. But another part of me worries that it will. I don't know what to do. You got any suggestions?"

"I don't know, Mom." I didn't exactly feel qualified to give advice on the subject.

"Of course you don't, dear," she said. "I shouldn't be unloading all this on you. It's my problem, my decision. I just needed to tell someone. And you're here."

"That's OK, Mom. I don't mind."

She walked over to the table where I was still sitting and patted my arm. "I don't mean to lean so hard on you, Matt. I know it's been rough on you the last few months, too. And I really do appreciate everything you're doing, all the extra responsibility you've taken on. You've shown a lot of maturity."

Her tears were starting again. "I love you very much, Matt."

My own eyes got misty. "I love you, too, Mom."

"And I'm very proud that you're my son." She grinned in an obvious attempt to lighten the moment and added, "But I want you to know that no matter how old and how big you get, you'll always be my little boy."

Something happened between us that night—or maybe it had been happening for a while and I didn't really understand it until that night. Mom was treating me like a man.

And while that was affirming on one level, it was disconcerting at the same time. I appreciated my mother's respect and her acceptance of me as an adult. I was glad for the responsibility and trust she gave me. It felt good that she could confide in me, that I could be a support and an encouragement to her. But it seemed that suddenly I was as much a friend as I was a son.

And despite what she said, I knew I couldn't ever be her little boy again. I didn't really want to be. Yet I couldn't help feeling like I was, in some strange way, losing my mom. And I'd already lost my dad.

I didn't know how many more changes I could take.

CHAPTER
10

Dad came by to take the three of us kids out for dinner the last Thursday evening of October. He got to the house ten minutes early, so when the doorbell rang, Mom opened the door. I walked into the front hallway just in time to overhear the exchange.

"Oh, hi," Mom said. "You're early. I thought it was one of Mark's friends at the door." She was obviously surprised. For weeks, Dad had been just pulling into the driveway, honking once and waiting in the car for us to come out. The two of them hadn't been face-to-face in some time.

Awkwardly, as if suddenly remembering her manners, Mom stepped back and said, "Come in."

Dad shook his head. "I just wanted to bring you this." He held out a sealed envelope. "I'd like you to read this after we've gone. Then maybe we should get together and talk about it."

"All right," Mom replied. And when she reached out quickly to take the envelope, I felt certain there was hope in her action. I felt some of that hope myself. *Could it be that Dad had finally come to his senses? That he wanted to make things right?* There was a seriousness, but also an air of anticipation in his expression.

"Melissa! Mark! Hurry up!" Mom called. "Your father's here!"

Dad retreated toward the car. I followed, pausing only a moment at the door to give Mom a good-bye peck on the cheek. Melissa and Mark caught up with me before I reached the driveway. And by the time Dad backed the car into the street, I felt sure Mom had ripped open the envelope and begun to read.

Dinner itself proved uneventful. Dad listened to the usual reports of school happenings, etc. But he seemed distracted, or at least subdued. Back at home he kissed Melissa and Mark good night and sent them on into the house. And the two of us sat in the front seat of his car.

"I want to tell you about the letter you saw me give your mother," he said.

"OK," I nodded. I wanted to know.

"I wrote your mother a long letter. I told her how sorry I was for what I'd put her through. What I put the whole family through. And I've asked her to forgive me."

That feeling of hope was there again. In the back of my mind. At the bottom of my heart.

"But . . . ," he paused.

Why did there have to be a but?

"But I also told her I thought we ought to think about pursuing a divorce. I don't see any other way out of this. And I told her why. I told her about Gwynn."

I guess I hadn't realized how much hope I'd had left.

Until that moment when I felt a sudden, gaping emptiness inside.

Dad seemed unsettled by my reaction, or rather my lack of reaction. I didn't say anything. I couldn't. I just stared through the windshield toward the broken backboard behind the house.

"I'm sorry, Matt," Dad finally said. "I wanted you to know. I figured you deserved to know. You're old enough to understand what—"

"I don't think I'll ever understand!" I cried as I shoved my door open and headed for the house.

When I reached the top of the stairs, I heard Mom in Mark's room, tucking him in. So I slipped down the hall to my own room and closed the door. I opened the physics book on my desk, but the homework problems all seemed to blur together. A few minutes later I heard Mom telling Melissa good night, and then there was a knock on my door.

"Can I come in?" Mom asked.

"Sure," I responded. I turned around to see her enter the room and close the door gently behind her.

"You didn't come in when Melissa and Mark did. You were talking with your father."

It wasn't a question. But I still replied, "Yes."

"He told you about his letter."

"Yes."

"Then you know that he thinks we ought to get a divorce?" Her voice wavered. I nodded.

"And you know about . . . ," She choked on the words. "You know why?"

I nodded again. And it was like I was giving permission for her to let go. She shuddered. Then she shook with huge convulsing sobs.

Instinctively I stood and walked toward her. I didn't know what to say, but I put my arms around her. Her entire body seemed to sag inward, and she slumped against me. The tears poured as if some inner dam had broken. Maybe it had.

Her pain made me want to cry. But I wouldn't. I wanted desperately to say something comforting. But I couldn't. All I could do was hold her, feeling her tears slowly soak my shoulder.

She seemed so hurt. So weak.

Gradually the sobs subsided. The tears stopped. And Mom stepped back to look at me with red-rimmed eyes. "I'm sorry, Matt," she said. "It's not as if this should have come as a big surprise. I even suspected there was someone else. . . ."

"You did?"

She nodded and wiped at a tear under her eye. "You don't live with someone for twenty years without being able to know when something goes wrong. Your father's letter didn't say when it started. But I knew something was wrong last spring . . . before Easter." She looked thoughtful as a long silence stretched out between us.

She finally wiped at her eyes then looked at me again. "You need to get some sleep, Matt. We both do. Things will look better in the morning."

I wasn't so sure. "You OK, Mom?"

She nodded. "I think so." She opened the door. But before she stepped out into the hall she turned to face me and forced a smile. "I guess I just needed a strong shoulder to cry on."

After she closed the door, I stripped off my shirt and laid it over the foot of my bed to dry.

The next night I took Jennifer to a home football

game at my school. Our team had only lost one game all year. Another victory would sew up a spot in the regional playoffs. So the excitement ran high from the opening kickoff. And the stands were rocking with every good play. When we scored a touchdown early in the third quarter, I leaped to my feet along with everyone else. But as everyone around me cheered or screamed in ecstasy, football suddenly seemed so insignificant to me. What difference would it make in the world that some guy in a white jersey carried an oblong ball through a mob of red jerseys and dove across a little white chalk line into a patch of grass called an end zone? What difference was that going to make in my life? Or my family's life?

The cheering continued through the subsequent kickoff and our following defensive series. The crowd remained standing, sensing victory. I leaned over close to Jennifer so she'd hear me over the noise. "Why don't we go?"

She thought she must have misunderstood. "What?"

"Let's cut out of here."

"Now?" she asked. I nodded.

"You sure?" she wanted to know. "I know this isn't my team, but I'm glad to stay till the end if you want to."

I shook my head. "OK," she said. And I took her hand as we eased our way down the bleachers to the ground.

Five minutes later we were driving out of the parking lot, and Jennifer was saying one more time, "We really could have stayed."

"I didn't feel much like cheering and screaming in a crowd of people," I said. "I'd rather be alone with you—some place where we can sit and talk."

"That sounds fine to me," Jennifer said.

"Wanna stop and get something to eat? McDougal's maybe?"

Jennifer groaned. "After the hot dog and popcorn at halftime, I'm stuffed."

"I'm not very hungry, either," I admitted.

"It must be serious," she said in a teasing voice. "I thought you were always hungry." When I failed to respond to her banter she got quiet. And after a couple of minutes of silence she said, "You've been pretty quiet all night. Is something wrong, Matt?"

I hadn't really planned on talking about it. And I certainly wasn't ready to talk about it driving down the road. But just ahead on the left side of the street was a huge office complex. The buildings were closed and the sprawling parking lot was deserted, so I turned in. I drove to the middle of the lot and pulled to a stop under a light pole with a burned-out bulb and cut the motor. Jennifer tucked one long leg up under her and leaned back against the passenger door. "You want to talk about it?"

I eased my head back against the seat and sighed. Finally I turned and looked at Jennifer. "I'm sorry. I didn't plan to ruin the evening. It's just that I couldn't go on pretending that a stupid football game really matters."

"It's OK," Jennifer said. I knew she wanted to ask what did matter, but she waited for me to say what was bothering me.

There didn't seem to be any way to ease into the subject, so I just said, "My dad wants to get a divorce."

"How do you know?"

"He told me last night. Told Mom, too. He even told her about his girlfriend." And I recounted the evening.

The envelope, the dinner with Dad, the conversation in his car, and then the scene with Mom in my room. When I finished by telling her what Mom said about needing a strong shoulder to cry on, Jennifer lifted my hand to her cheek and then kissed it. "You do have strong shoulders, Matt," she said gently.

I shook my head. "Then why do I feel so weak, so helpless?"

When I said that, Jennifer swung around on the seat and leaned across me to put her head on my left shoulder and her left arm around my neck. I knew she meant it as a warm, reassuring gesture, but the moment I put my arms around her and felt her head against the shoulder Mom had cried on, all the feelings of the previous night surged up from deep inside me, and the tears I'd held in for Mom came pouring out. I'd never cried in front of Jennifer before. I hadn't cried in front of any girl since second grade. The cascade of emotion embarrassed me, but I couldn't stop it.

Jennifer didn't say anything. She just held on to me. And as the tears slowed to a trickle, I felt the warmth of her fingers gently stroking the hair at the back of my neck.

Finally I sniffled and cleared my throat. "I'm sorry," I said. "That was a pretty wimpy thing to do."

Jennifer sat up. Our faces were six inches apart. There was just enough light for me to see the trail of tears running down her face as she looked into my eyes. "Matt Guthrie," she said, "I think you're not only the most sensitive guy I've ever known, but you're also the strongest."

"Right!" I said sarcastically. "That's why I'm sitting here blubbering like a baby."

She jabbed me in the ribs. "Don't be such a macho

dummy. It takes a strong person to let feelings out like that. Don't be embarrassed by it. I'm not. I'm crying because I'm so happy that you trust me enough to cry in front of me."

I laughed. "Maybe I'll bring some onions to cut up next time we go out."

She grinned and sniffled. "I'd rather you kissed me," she said. So I did.

The moment our lips met I went weak all over. But seconds later I felt as if I could tear phone books in half or rip chains for her.

I'd kissed Jennifer before. But not like this. I'd never kissed anyone quite like this. Or been kissed like it. It felt like our bodies were melting together.

When we finally stopped to catch our breaths, Jennifer leaned her head against my chest. "I can hear your heart beating," she said softly as I traced the side of her face with my finger. Then I kissed her cheek and her ear and her neck—and she lifted her head and our lips met again.

It was incredible. Nothing else mattered. Nothing else existed. It was as if my whole being focused on that kiss and I lost awareness of anything else. Yet at the same time every nerve ending in me tingled with intense awareness of my body. And of Jennifer's body.

The third kiss was more passionate yet. And when Jennifer slid her hand under my sweater and up my back I flinched involuntarily and kissed her harder. I didn't know any touch could be so electric. Instinctively I slid my own hand up along her ribs. When she flinched and stiffened I moved my hand away. She pulled back for a second and then put her head against my shoulder again, pulling her hand from under my sweater as she did so. I didn't want to stop. And that realization of the power of my passion both excited and scared me.

The windows were steaming over and everything was quiet. Except for the continued pounding of my heart.

Finally I broke the silence. "I'm sorry," I said hesitantly. "I guess I got carried away."

"It's OK," Jennifer whispered softly. "You weren't the only one. I was the one who started it."

Again we were quiet, until she said, "A penny for your thoughts."

"I was thinking about your mother."

She laughed as she said, "My mother?"

"What she told you. About how men only want one thing. And I'm hoping you don't think. . . ."

Jennifer shushed me by sitting up and putting a finger to my lips. "What I really think," she said, "is that my mother should have warned me that sometimes girls want the same thing." She laid her head gently against my shoulder again.

All those feelings came back. The warmth. The weakness. The strength. And I said for the first time what I'd known for a long time. "I love you very much Jennifer. I think I started to love you that first night we went out, when we played miniature golf. You were so beautiful, and yet I felt so comfortable. You drew me out, you listened to me. And I started to love you right—" This time she shushed me with another long kiss.

Then it was quiet again for a time. And when I looked at my watch I couldn't believe the time. I started the car and waited for the defroster to clear the windshield.

We were both quiet on the drive to Jennifer's house.

She leaned her head against my shoulder. And my mind raced back over the past five months. Five months was all it had been. But so much had happened. And Jennifer had been there for me. I walked her to the door and kissed her good night. But before she turned to go inside, I held her shoulders.

"I want you to know I meant what I said. I really do love you."

"I know," she said.

"But I don't just love you. I need you. You listen to me when I'm hurting. You care about what I care about. You make me feel strong and loved. Like tonight. I was so down, feeling so discouraged and helpless. And you made me feel so great. Maybe too great there for a little while." I grinned and she pulled close and put her head back on my shoulder.

"I needed you tonight. I needed your love, your strength. I guess I've needed you for the past five months. And I don't want to ever lose you."

She kissed me once more before she said, "And I don't want to lose you either." And she wiped at her eyes.

"I don't think you ever have to worry about that," I said. "You're too wonderful. Too perfect for me to let you go."

I could see her tears glistening in the porchlight as she shook her head. "Don't be so sure, Matt. I'm not that wonderful."

She had turned and disappeared into the house before her words really hit. I wished I knew what prompted them. Something about her response troubled me, but I didn't spend a lot of time thinking about it. There were too many other feelings to sort out that night.

CHAPTER

11

I'd been worried all along about what would happen when Mom found out the whole truth about Dad. Maybe I shouldn't have been. I'd halfway expected her to go into another depression like she'd had when Dad first moved out. But she didn't.

One night early the next week she asked me to be at home to watch Mark for a couple of hours. "I'm going to see a marriage counselor," she said.

"Is Dad going with you?"

She shook her had sadly. "I tried to get him to go, but he said it was no use."

"Then why—"

"Because," Mom interrupted my question, "I need to talk about this with someone, someone who's a professional. I need to understand my own feelings. This woman is a Christian counselor whom the pastor highly recommends."

Mom went to the counselor once a week for the next few weeks. A couple of times when she got home her eyes were red, and her face looked as if she'd been crying. But I think counseling was good for her. She seemed surprisingly strong. She acted less tired in the evenings, and she even talked less about the little problems at work. Her boss had left her alone after that one incident, and she was enjoying her job again.

I know Mom didn't want a divorce. She told me she'd been trying to talk Dad out of it. Evidently she kept asking him to go with her to counseling. I never saw them talking. They must have communicated by phone because Mom told me one night that Dad was moving ahead toward a divorce, and she had to see a lawyer the next afternoon.

Time was running out.

Gary Maxwell, the church's youth minister gave me a call about the middle of November. "It's been a while since you and I talked," he said. "How about if we have breakfast at McDonald's before school on Thursday? I'll pick you up anytime you say."

The prospect didn't excite me, but it seemed rude to turn him down. "Sure," I agreed. "How 'bout seven o'clock?"

"Sounds fine. See ya then."

Gary went through the drive-up and we sat in the car to eat. I was glad for the extra privacy because I knew he was going to want to talk about my family. And sure enough, we finished the small talk about the time I took the last bite of my Egg McMuffin. Then he asked me how things were going at home.

I told him Dad was pushing for a divorce, and Mom had her own lawyer now.

"How are you doing with all this?" he wanted to know.

"OK, I guess." I didn't really know Gary all that

well and didn't feel like talking about my emotions.

"How are you doing spiritually?"

No point in lying about it. "Not that great."

Gary wiped his mouth with a napkin and asked, "You want to elaborate on that?"

"I don't know." I closed up my styrofoam food container and dropped it into the empty paper bag. "I guess I just don't feel much like praying or reading the Bible."

"I think I can understand that," he said. "But I'd like to hear it in your words. Why do you think that is?"

I didn't know if he understood or not, and I didn't feel like talking about it. But I had to say something. So I told him the truth. "I guess I don't feel much like praying or reading the Bible because I don't think it's any use. When my dad first left home, I prayed every day and every night that he'd come back. But he didn't. For the past six months, I've prayed off and on that my parents would get back together, that Dad would change his mind. But it's done no good at all. It looks now like my dad's going to file for divorce in a couple of weeks. And I don't think all the praying in the world is going to stop him."

"Maybe not," Gary said. And then he was quiet for a full minute, as if he was trying to decide what to say. "You know," he finally said, "one of the hardest things for me to understand about God is why he lets people mess up the world. Why he lets people hurt themselves and hurt other people. We want things to be perfect. But God always gives us the choice of doing right or wrong. It's our choice.

"You can pray that your dad will change his mind. And I'll pray with you, Matt. But God won't change your dad's mind unless he's ready to have it changed.

God doesn't work like that. The choice will be up to your dad."

Then what good is prayer? I thought bleakly. *What good is God if he won't do something as basic, as important, as keeping a family together?* But I didn't say that out loud. I didn't say anything.

Gary went on. "Nobody is perfect. You're not perfect. I'm not perfect. Your dad's not perfect. People will always let us down. But it's important to remember that that's because we're all human. You can't trust human beings to always make the right decision. But you can always trust God. Because he loves us and always wants what's best for us.

"The Bible doesn't promise that Christians will always have it easy. It doesn't say everything will go our way if we pray hard enough. But God does promise that if we stick close to him he will always be with us and give us the help and strength to endure whatever the world throws at us, whatever problems or disappointments we face."

He paused. "Sorry. Didn't mean to preach you a sermon." I smiled, and soon we were on our way to the school.

I thought about what Gary said for the rest of the day. I wanted to believe it. But I wasn't sure I did. So that night, lying in bed, I prayed—really prayed—for the first time in a long time. I told God I was having a hard time believing in him, or at least believing he cared. And I challenged him. "OK, Lord," I prayed. "If Dad doesn't change his mind, and if you expect me to keep believing in you, you're going to have to give me the help and strength to deal with it." That was it. That was my prayer.

Dad didn't change his mind. The last week of

November, when he took us three kids out for dinner, he told us the papers would be going to the judge the next week. "Then you and Mom will be divorced?" Melissa asked.

"No," Dad shook his head. "The divorce won't be final until thirty days later. Right after the first of the year."

Melissa began to cry, but I didn't feel any reaction. I was becoming resigned to what looked like the inevitable.

Mom seemed resigned, too. The night before she and Dad went to court, she called a family meeting in the living room. She explained what was going to be happening, that nothing would be final for thirty days. "But I want you to know that you'll still have a mom and a dad," she said. "And we both love you very much."

She explained that they'd agreed to share joint custody, and that Dad wanted to continue to support us financially. There wasn't going to be any big nasty battle in court. "You'll keep on living with me," she said. "But you'll be able to see your father every week just like you've been doing. And you can go over to his apartment whenever you want." She asked if we had any questions, but none of us did.

The papers were filed. Everything moved ahead. And for the first year ever, Christmas vacation came too soon.

Mom and Dad did their best to have a normal family Christmas. As normal as we could under the circumstances.

Mark had us all awake by 6:30 A.M. But we had to wait until Dad got to the house about seven to start anything. Dad asked me to help him carry in a pile of presents from his car. When we added them to the pile already under the tree it looked like the biggest Christmas I ever remembered. I played Santa and started handing out presents one at a time for people to open. We didn't unwrap the last package until after eight.

"There's one more thing," Dad announced. "It's for Matt. But he'll have to come outside to get it." So we all put on our coats. I tried to figure out what it could be as we headed out the door. Dad led us around the front of the house and back to the driveway. And then I saw it.

A new backboard and rim leaned against the goal support behind the house. There was a big green ribbon tied around it and a red bow stuck right in the middle of the square.

"Thanks, Dad," I said.

"You're welcome," he said. "First warm day, give me a call, and I'll come over and help you put it up."

"All right," I promised.

We all went back inside, and Dad helped Mark put together the electric race car track he'd bought him. Dad didn't stay for Christmas dinner. Actually none of us did. Mom and the three of us kids drove out to Grandpa and Grandma's for a big afternoon feast. Grandma's cooking was as wonderful as ever, but I couldn't help thinking about other family Christmases and realizing Christmas would never be the same again.

Friday, January 7, was a winter day like any winter day. The bells rang at the end of every class. There was a pep rally for the basketball team in the gym just before the end of school. And I walked the two blocks home at the end of the day.

Mom was home already. She'd planned to take the

afternoon off to go the courthouse for the signing of the final settlement. She met me coming in the front door and I knew by the sadness in her eyes that it was finally over. Once again I had no words. But I gave Mom a hug on my way to my room to read my Lit homework.

When I finally went back downstairs again, Mom was fixing supper and listening to a network news show. There was a short clip about farm economy in the Midwest, a comment about an earthquake in South America, and an in-depth report on new tensions in the Middle East.

But the worst event of the day didn't make the World News Tonight.

Supper was quiet. Melissa was at a friend's. Mom didn't say anything about what happened at the courthouse, and I didn't ask. As soon as we finished eating, I cleared the table, started the dishwasher, and headed back to my room.

I'd really thought I was ready. For a month I'd known when it was going to happen. I didn't expect anything to stop it. I'd accepted the inevitable.

So as I lay on my bed, staring blankly at the circle of light my bedside lamp cast on the ceiling, the power of my feelings staggered me. Everything I thought I'd put behind me, every emotion I'd felt for the past seven months, came flooding back. The hurt, the grief, the anger, the strangled hope, and the helpless despair. It was all there.

I'd thought I'd begun to heal. *So much for God's help and strength!* I thought bleakly.

Mom was so depressed the next day that the whole house felt like a mortuary. By the time I left to pick up Jennifer for a date Saturday night, I felt like breaking windows and knocking down walls.

Once again Jennifer was the perfect prescription. We went to a drama club play at her school. Sitting in the darkness of that auditorium, holding tightly to her hand, feeling her warmth, her life, I actually forgot about my family for an hour. I even laughed at the comedy on stage.

Afterwards we talked. I gave her a report of the previous day, including my surprising emotions. "It was like the wound was ripped open again, and all the festering feelings came gushing out."

She scooted over against me in the front car seat and gently took my right hand, intertwining her fingers with mine. "I think that's a pretty good analogy," she said. "I remember feeling that way several times after my parents' divorce. When the divorce was final. Again when my father got remarried. And when he called to say he was moving to Texas. And then the first year he forgot to call me on my birthday.

"Each time it hurt a little less. The feelings weren't as intense. I guess the wounds heal pretty slow. But I think mine are mostly healed now."

I didn't respond to that. I just thought about what she'd said. And after a time I said, "I guess what makes it so painful is being hurt by someone you care so much about. It seems so stupid, so wrong. I know my dad loves me, and he loves Melissa and Mark so much. And yet I can't ever imagine being more hurt than he hurt me. Than he hurt all of us. How can a person hurt someone he loves so much?"

"I don't know," Jennifer responded quietly.

"I don't either. But I'm gonna make sure I never ever hurt anyone like that. And I promise you that I'll never hurt you as long as we live. I don't know what I'd ever do without you. I need you Jennifer. And I love you so much."

She leaned up and sweetly kissed my cheek. "I don't ever want to hurt you either, Matt." And then she was quiet for a long, long time.

CHAPTER 12

Dad picked us up the last Thursday night of January. When we piled into the car, he turned to Melissa and asked, "Where do you want to eat tonight? It's your choice."

She thought for a minute. "How 'bout Red Lobster?"

"Good choice," Dad grinned. "Red Lobster it is!"

But when he hung a left at the end of the street, Mark immediately piped up: "We're going the wrong way."

"Don't worry. We're going to make one quick stop before we go to the restaurant," Dad said.

We drove to the other side of town. But I didn't begin to suspect anything until we pulled into an apartment complex parking lot and Dad left us with the assurance he'd be right back out in five minutes. Even though I guessed whose apartment he was going to, I wasn't prepared three minutes later when I saw her emerge from the building walking briskly alongside Dad.

She was tall; with heels she stood almost as tall as

Dad. She walked with the easy grace of an athlete or a model, her long blonde hair bouncing on her shoulders with each stride. As they hurried toward the car, I couldn't help thinking Dad looked out of place beside her.

Dad opened the front passenger door and motioned Mark into the back with Melissa and me. The woman slid in, and there was an awkward silence from the time Dad closed her door until he walked around the front of the car and climbed in his seat. Dad turned and smiled around the headrest of his bucket seat.

"This is Gwynn. I wanted her to meet you all, so she's going to dinner with us tonight. That's Mark right behind you. Melissa. And Matt."

"Hi," she said. "I'm glad to finally get to meet you all. Your dad has told me a lot about you. Now I can see why he's so proud of you."

Her voice was as silky as it had sounded the first time I'd heard it on the tape in Dad's apartment. And as the memory of that moment flooded back into my mind, I turned my eyes from the smiling face looking back at me and focused out the window.

Dad tried to cover the awkwardness with a running monologue that lasted most of the way to the restaurant. He filled Gwynn in on each of our interests in school and sports.

After the waitress took all our orders, Dad tried to jumpstart a conversation by telling us, "Gwynn just got back from a ski vacation out in Colorado."

"You like to ski?" Mark asked.

She nodded. "Very much. It's one of my favorite things in the whole world."

"Do you go all the way to the top of the mountains?" Mark wanted to know.

She laughed. "Not quite. But I like to go all the way to the top of the ski trails."

"Gwynn used to be a competitive ski racer," Dad interjected with a touch of pride.

"But that was a long time ago," she added. "I haven't trained since I left college."

I wondered how long ago college had been. I guessed she was probably in her early thirties; she was an experienced lawyer. But she looked more like twenty-six or twenty-seven. Her hands, especially the long tapered fingers deftly shelling her appetizer of cold boiled shrimp, looked young. *She's almost as close to my age as she is to Dad's.* For some reason I couldn't get that thought out of my mind.

There wasn't much conversation during dinner. Though Dad made a continuous effort, first with her and then in turn with each of us. I think even Mark felt the awkwardness. And when we finished our entrees and Melissa excused herself to make a trip to the bathroom, I don't think she was very happy to hear Gwynn say, "Wait, I'll go with you."

Dad watched them cross the restaurant. So did I. For that matter, so did half the other men in the place. And for the first time I realized that a woman my dad thought was attractive seemed attractive to me, too. The thought made me feel more awkward than I had before. It seemed somehow wrong, almost perverted. Not just for me, but for Dad as well. He didn't belong with any young sexy skier; he belonged with Mom. And he always would.

Back in the car again, Gwynn asked me my plans for the coming year. When I said I was going to college, she asked: "Where?"

"I'm not sure yet. I've applied to a couple of places,"

I told her, "but I haven't decided."

She asked if I knew what I wanted to major in.

"No. That's the problem. I'd like to get into computer science. But I'm also interested in journalism."

"They're both interesting fields," she said.

Dad spoke up. "That's the trouble with a kid who has too many talents. Can't decide what he'd do best at." He grinned at me.

We dropped Gwynn off first. Mark climbed quickly into the front seat the moment she got out. And everything seemed almost normal again by the time we got home. Dad kissed Mark and Melissa good night.

"I'm sorry it was so awkward tonight," Dad said as the two kids trotted into the house.

"It might have helped if you'd given us a little warning," I told him.

"Maybe," he admitted. "But she didn't know if she'd be free until this afternoon. And I wanted you to meet her."

"She seems nice." I had to say something.

"When you get to know her better I think you'll like her," he said.

"I gotta go. Got a test tomorrow."

Dad reached out and gave my shoulder a squeeze. "Give me a call when you want to put that backboard up."

"OK," I said, heading for the door.

Jennifer called the first Tuesday afternoon in February. "You got anything planned for tomorrow night?"

"Nothing. What's up?"

"I just found out today that Mr. Hamann, one of the counselors at my school, wants to start a small discussion group for students from divorced families. When

I went in to sign up I asked if I could bring a friend from another school, and Mr. Hamann said it'd be all right. And I'd like you to come with me."

"I don't know." Sitting in a room with a bunch of strangers I didn't know and talking about something as personal as my parents' divorce didn't sound like a great idea. "I wouldn't know anyone there."

"You'd know me."

"That doesn't count."

"Oh. So I don't count?"

"You know what I mean, Jennifer. I just don't know that I want to talk about my parents' divorce."

"You talk to me."

"That's different," I said.

"I think I ought to go."

"Then go."

"I'd like some company. If you don't feel comfortable, you don't have to say anything. You won't have to worry what anyone else thinks because you won't know them anyway. And if you decide not to go to another meeting I promise never to say another word about it. OK?"

"You sure you want to do this?"

"I didn't say I wanted to. I said I thought I ought to. There's a difference. I think you ought to, too. Please?"

"Just once, right?"

"Unless you decide to go again."

"Don't count on it."

"OK."

"OK," I echoed. "I'll go with you." And I regretted the words the moment they passed my lips.

When Jennifer and I walked into the classroom the next evening, there were only two students and the counselor who walked over to greet me. "I'm Jeff

Hamann. You're Jennifer's friend from Jefferson High School?"

"Matt Guthrie." We shook hands.

"Glad you could come, Matt. Have a seat. We're expecting a few more people."

There were ten of us, including Mr. Hamann, when he finally stood and began the meeting. He explained that one reason he wanted to start this group was because his own parents had gotten a divorce when he was fourteen. So he understood how tough it could be to have a family break up. But he also said that he knew, both from experience and from his work and study as a counselor, that one of the best ways of working through the problems caused by a divorce was to talk about the experience and the feelings—as hard as that seemed. He said he didn't want anyone to feel pressured to talk if they didn't want to. (That sounded good to me.) He spent the next fifteen minutes or so telling about his parents' divorce and about his feelings at the time.

He finally paused and looked around the room. "What about some of you? How did you feel when your parents divorced?"

Everyone was quiet for so long I figured we all might just as well head home. But then a girl named Angela spoke up. "I remember one night when I was eleven. They went into their bedroom and closed the door. I could hear them talking so I went to the door to listen. When I heard the word *divorce*, I hurried away; I didn't want to hear it. I got up the next morning to find my mom crying. My dad kissed my good-bye and just left."

Angela's voice was filled with emotion. The memory was so obviously painful that I couldn't believe she'd go on. But she did.

"I had never suspected anything. I thought my parents fought like everyone else's parents. I was confused and depressed for a couple of years. I quit doing things with my friends. I'd come home after school and mope around the house.

"At times I'd go to my room, pull a pillow over my head, and just scream. My dad wasn't there when I didn't get along with my mom, and she wasn't any help in my relationship with him. I got to the point where I thought I was going to have a nervous breakdown or something. A couple of times I told my mom I was going to kill myself because I didn't feel anybody loved me. Grades and school didn't matter anymore. What I wanted was a loving family. Everything else seemed so pointless."

When Angela finished talking, Mr. Hamann thanked her for sharing and asked if anyone else had anything to say. I glanced over at Jennifer, but she was staring straight ahead, deep in her own thoughts.

A guy named Brad talked next. "For me the divorce was a big relief. My dad was an alcoholic. I remember waking in the middle of the night and hearing my parents screaming. My dad would be drunk and throwing things. As a little kid I remember being very scared—and very relieved when we moved out."

There was hardly a pause before the next person spoke up. "My parents divorced when I was a baby," explained Mitzi. "So I don't remember any feelings from the time. But once I got older and started asking questions and understanding what had happened, I blamed my mom. It seemed she didn't do anything to save the marriage. I kept thinking, 'If only she'd tried, maybe we'd all be together as a family today.'"

Mr. Hamann nodded. "OK. Anyone else?" As he shifted his gaze around the room, I lowered mine. "Allen, you looked like you were going to say something a minute ago."

A big guy, who I found out later was a football lineman, nodded. "My parents' divorce wasn't exactly a surprise because they'd been separated for a long time. But I still had a lot of bitterness toward my father when the divorce finally went through. In fact, I once punched a hole in my bedroom wall out of sheer frustration." I got a flashing image of a basketball rim being ripped off a backboard as Allen went on. "I'd look around at my friends and see the things, the opportunities I didn't have. And I'd think, 'If my dad were here, we wouldn't have these problems.' Or 'If he were around, I wouldn't have to work just to help Mom pay the bills.'"

"OK, good," Mr. Hamann said. "You've mentioned a variety of emotions: depression, confusion, anger, relief, bitterness. Any other emotions you want to mention?"

"Grief," said Jennifer. "You're actually losing a family."

"Guilt," someone else added.

"Right," the counselor agreed. "That's an especially common reaction of young children. They assume it's somehow their fault. Anything else?"

"Hopelessness." I didn't catch who said it.

"I think we've all felt that," Mr. Hamann said. "I know I did." He waited for a few seconds before continuing. "At another meeting maybe we can come back and talk in more detail about some of these common emotional reactions. But tonight I'd like to move on to another question just to get you thinking. It's this: What are some of the struggles of living in a single-parent family?"

Angela was first again. "You're forced to be independent and to take more responsibility around the house. Just last week I had to use a knife to fix the oven. And most one-parent families don't have as much money, so I've had to do without a lot of stuff my friends have. My mom can't afford to buy my clothes, so all the money I make from my part-time job goes for clothes. And that means I usually don't have much spending money."

"I sometimes feel jealous of other people," Cindi admitted. "When I hear kids complain because their dads won't allow them a later curfew, or won't let them have the car or whatever, I'm afraid I don't have much sympathy. At least they have a dad to not give them a later curfew."

Brad said, "I remember everybody sort of taking care of themselves. Mom had to work full time, so ever since I was in third grade I've had to get myself and my younger sister to the bus stop on time. The added responsibility made me feel different from other kids. It made me feel lonely; no one else seemed to be at my level."

A girl named Laura spoke up for the first time. "I think I always got away with more stuff than I would have if I'd had two parents at home. Mom was just too busy and too tired to always keep a tight rein. So I think one of the toughest things is the wear and tear on the single parent. It makes you feel bad to see your parent always on the verge of exhaustion."

"Another thing," it was Angela again, "I remember

watching *The Brady Bunch* on TV when I was younger and seeing how they always used to get together and have dinner. This might be because I'm an only child, but living with just my mom, it seems we've lost that feel of being a family. It's more like living with a friend. The infrequent times we do sit down to eat dinner together, it doesn't feel like a family. The only time I get that feeling is when we get together with other relatives."

"Thanks, Angela," Mr. Hamann responded. "I'm sure we could go on. And we will another time. But I wanted to cover a lot of territory quickly tonight just to give you all a feel for the kinds of things we'll be talking about in this group. So let me get a little reaction. How many of you have heard someone else say something tonight you could have said, something you identified with?" Every person in the room raised a hand. "Good. Then how many of you think it's helpful to hear other people express feelings like this?" Again we all raised a hand.

"One last question. I'd like to have another meeting in two weeks and then decide whether there's enough interest on your parts to meet twice a month for the rest of the school year. So how many of you would plan to come back again in two weeks?"

Hands went up quickly around the room. I looked over at Jennifer and slowly raised my hand. She grinned and winked at me.

"Great," exclaimed Mr. Hamann. "Then we'll see you two weeks from tonight. But before you go I'd like to say one more thing. One of the best ways to understand your own feelings and reactions to your parents' divorce is to compare your experience with other peoples' experiences. A group like this is a great place to start. But if you'd like to get an even broader sampling of experiences, I'd recommend a couple of books that report a number of kids' experiences." He held up two books.

"I'm not recommending these as advice books. Merely as samples of other people's reactions. Some will be different from your experience. Some will be similar. But they can help you better identify and understand your feelings, and they may give you more to share next time we get together. They aren't assigned reading. But if you want to find out about more experiences like we've heard tonight, check the school library or the public library for these books. See you in two weeks."

I read both of the books before the next meeting. And they did the same thing the meeting did for me. They validated my own reactions. Everything I'd felt for the past eight months was mentioned in those books or in the meeting. My feelings were normal. I'd wanted to believe it—now I had proof. And that proof of normality was a weight off my mind, a weight I hadn't realized was so heavy until it was gone.

It didn't take away the feelings. I still felt helpless to make the situation right again between my parents. I still felt angry and frustrated by what Dad did. I still didn't know how to restore the relationship I used to have with my dad, or if I'd ever be able to. But I now knew all these emotions were common reactions, experienced by others who'd been through the break-up of their parents. That alone gave me a confidence and a sense of determined optimism I hadn't known for months. I finally knew I was going to survive.

Then the next bombshell hit.

CHAPTER

13

"Can I talk to you for a few minutes, Matt?" I turned from the homework on my desk to see Mom standing at the door of my room.

"Sure. Come on in."

Mom walked in and sat gingerly on the edge of my bed. I swivelled my chair to face her.

"What's up?"

She didn't say anything for a few seconds. Then she looked up at me with a tentative smile. "I keep trying to think of a way to make this easier," she said. "But I can't."

What now? I wondered. A sudden sense of apprehension tightened up inside me as I silently waited for her to go on.

"I've been doing a lot of thinking about our situation the last few months. . . ."

Of course.

"You know things have been pretty tight financially.

And I've been talking to a number of people about that. . . ."

OK. But what's the point?

"It looks like the wisest thing for us to do right now would be to move."

"Move?" The idea was a stunning, blind-side blow.

"We've got a lot of equity in the house," Mom hurried right on. "We could find something with lower monthly payments."

"Move where?" I didn't care about the reasons.

"I don't know for sure. Probably near Grandma and Grandpa. Near my job. There are some nice new townhouses out there. They'd be affordable and nice. They wouldn't have the maintenance and yard work we have here."

"But I do the yard work. And I can paint and do stuff that needs to be done around the house."

Mom smiled and nodded. "You've been a terrific help the last few months. But you're going to college next year. Then it'll just be Melissa, Mark, and me. We need to be thinking about that, about the future. I've been praying about it a lot the past couple of weeks, asking God to give me some kind of leading or indication about what we ought to do. And I think the best option seems to be moving."

"When would we have to move?"

"That's the other thing. I figured we could put the house up for sale this spring and hope to move this summer when—"

"So soon?"

"Well, that's what I was thinking," she hesitated, "before today."

"What happened today?"

"I just pulled into the driveway this afternoon, when

Mr. and Mrs. Drake from down the street walked by with another couple. It was Mrs. Drake's sister and her husband who are moving here from California in a few weeks. They are looking for a home and they'd like to find one near the Drakes. Mrs. Drake asked me if I knew of any houses in our neighborhood that might be going up for sale soon. And I said, 'As a matter of fact, I do.'

"They came in and looked around the house. They really liked it. When they asked how much I'd sell for, I had no idea what to say. I told them I'd get back to them first thing in the morning and then I called United Realty and talked to Judy Powell from church. She said she'd do some checking to see what other houses have sold for in our neighborhood in the last year, and she's coming over to take a look at the house tonight. She'll help set the price with no obligation. And if the Drake's relatives agree to buy it, we'll be able to sell it without having to pay a broker's commission and without even having to go through the hassle of putting the house on the market. It would be a wonderful answer to prayer."

How can God answer Mom's prayers and not answer any of mine? I thought. Besides, I could see nothing wonderful about it. "When would we have to move?"

Mom shrugged. "I don't know for sure. I have to do some checking. If we can't find a place to move to soon enough, we might have to move in with Grandma and Grandpa for a few weeks as an interim arrangement. I don't know. But the Collinses, that's the Drakes' relatives, have already sold their old house and want to move here in a month or so."

"A month? Mom, I'm in the middle of my last semester of high school! It's the absolute worst time of my life to change schools!"

"I know that, Matt. That's why I had to talk to you. To let you know what's happening. How miraculous it was that I 'just happened' to run into the Drakes today. That Mrs. Drake 'just happened' to ask if I knew of any house going up for sale. You can see God's hand in this, can't you, Matt?"

"I don't know about that." *If God's hand is in this, it's slapping me across the face*. "What I do know is that I can't change schools. Not now!"

"Maybe you won't have to."

I looked quickly at Mom. "What do you mean?"

"I don't know," she admitted. "But maybe we can work something out. You'd just have three months or so to finish up. I'll call the school office tomorrow and see what the possibilities are. If the Lord can work out the sale of the house, he can work that out, too. Right?"

"Sure." There was more sarcasm than conviction in my response, but I don't think Mom noticed. The doorbell rang at about that instant, and she hurried out to see who it was.

I heard her talking to someone down in the living room. A few minutes later I heard someone climbing the stairs. "This is the largest bedroom other than the master," Mom was saying. "Each bedroom has a large window and double-door closets. This is Matt's room—you know Matt."

When I turned to see Judy Powell behind Mom, I stood and said, "Hi, Mrs. Powell."

"Hello, Matt," she replied. A couple of minutes later, after she'd looked in my closet, they left and proceeded to Melissa's room. I didn't follow them. I just lay down on my bed and tried to focus on the ceiling. Once again my life had taken a sudden, unexpected turn and was hurtling out of my control.

"So your mom worked it out?" Jennifer asked as we drove to her school for our second meeting with Mr. Hamann's discussion group.

"I won't know for sure until next week, but it looks like it. The assistant principal told her the board had made exceptions before in cases like mine where someone's family moves during their senior year. Usually the students stay in the district with a friend or relative. In my case, I'd be commuting. That's the only hitch. But it looks like it'll be OK."

"You don't sound very excited."

"I'm not. My first reaction to the idea of moving was completely negative. I thought the reason was school, because that was the first implication I considered. But once it looked like a move wouldn't have to disrupt my last semester of school, I realized I don't want to move for a lot of reasons. I grew up in my neighborhood. In that house. I have a lot of memories stored away there. And most of them are good ones. Memories I don't want to let go or lose."

"If I've learned one thing about moving it's that memories are portable," Jennifer said. "You can take the good ones wherever you go. And the bad ones tag along whether you want them or not."

I glanced over at Jennifer and shook my head. "You know what I mean. Places have memories, too."

"Sure. Sometimes too many. And maybe that's one reason your mom wants to move. So that some of her memories can be stored away and don't have to be in plain sight every day."

"You could be right. I hadn't thought about it from her perspective. I should have."

"Sometimes moving can be like a fresh start," Jennifer said thoughtfully. "Some people need that.

You're going to college next year. For you, that'll be like a fresh start. Your mom won't have that. Moving could really help her."

"OK, could be," I admitted. "But it doesn't make moving any more appealing or any easier for me."

"Nobody said it did," Jennifer replied. "Change, even necessary change, is usually hard."

I looked over at Jennifer again. She looked and sounded so serious. "You're sounding like a psychoanalyst again."

She didn't return my grin. "Sorry. I didn't mean to."

"It's OK," I assured her as we drove into the school parking lot. Two students who'd come to the first meeting didn't show. But there were two new people, Ryan and Beth. So there were still ten in all. Mr. Hamann asked us to introduce ourselves again. Then he began the meeting by saying that, like the first meeting, this would be a rather general discussion. We would touch on a variety of subjects to help us get a feel for one another and for the problems revolving around divorce. He promised that at the end of the meeting we'd set a tentative subject to talk more in-depth about next time we got together.

"Let's start tonight by coming at the subject from a little different angle," said Mr. Hamann. "What positive effects do you think your parents' divorce may have had on you?"

"Independence," said Beth and several other people nodded. "I've had to learn to do a lot of things for myself. And while I haven't always enjoyed the extra responsibility, I know it's taught me to be a more independent person. I know that when I graduate from college and set out on my own, I won't be running home to my parents every time I have a little problem."

"I agree with Beth," Angela added. "I think my experience has helped me grow up quicker than I would have."

Brad said, "I think it's forced me to open up more with friends. With Dad gone and Mom working all day, if I wanted to talk to anyone besides my little sister, I was out of luck. Unless I talked with a friend."

"I think my experience has helped give me a direction in life," added Phyllis. "I'd like to spend my life helping people who are going through what I went through. That's one reason I signed up for these meetings. I'd like to go into some sort of family counseling career. I think my experience has helped me be a more sensitive person. I know what it's like to hurt."

A couple of other people shared before Mr. Hamann changed course. "How many people here have step-parents?" Over half the group raised their hands. "What have you learned about getting along with step-parents?"

"Only that it's impossible," Ryan said and a couple of people laughed in obvious agreement.

"Would you like to elaborate?" Mr. Hamann asked.

"Sure," Ryan said. "Living with a parent and a step-parent forces you to be so stinking mature. You're always walking a fine line between the two of them, trying to decide which instructions to follow and which to ignore."

"He's right," agreed Phyllis. "You're never sure who's in charge. Sometimes both parents try to be and they contradict each other. Other times neither of them will take responsibility for something you need to have done. You have to be ready to stick up for your rights if a step-parent does something wrong. But at the same time, you ought to let them know when they do something great."

Allen said, "It's tough. Your mom is your mom and your step-father is just this guy who comes to live with you. It's hard to accept that sometimes."

I looked at Jennifer as she said, "It's also hard to accept when your step-parent seems to take the place of your entire family. When your father gives all his attention to his new wife, and their children, and pretty much writes you off. It's hard not feeling jealous and bitter." When she said that, I realized Jennifer and I hadn't talked much about her ongoing feelings toward her father; we'd spent a lot more time talking about my feelings toward my father. And I felt guilty about that.

"At first I didn't get along at all with my step-dad," Cindi admitted. "But one day I decided I really needed to work on my attitude. So I started talking to him more, listening to him, asking his opinions on things, having real conversations with him. And this past Valentine's Day I was getting a card for my sister and my mom when I decided to get something for him, too. I'd never done anything like that before, so I didn't know what kind of card to get. I didn't feel right giving him one that said, 'To Dad.' So I settled for one that said, 'You're a special person', and I wrote a little something on it. Later I found out he told my mom, 'Cindi's really a thoughtful girl.'

"I'd thought all my time and effort at being nice was going down the drain. But it's not. I've noticed a nice change in our relationship that is improving things for the whole family."

"I think you have to look at your relationship with a step-parent more as a friendship relationship," added Phyllis. "They can't take the place of a parent. But you can treat them like a friend. You need to be respectful and can't treat them like they don't belong. Once they are married to one of your parents, they are part of the family. You need to do your best to get along."

The group talked some about the problems of visitation. One of the girls, I don't remember which, said she felt like a bag lady, shuffling clothes and belongings back and forth on weekends and holidays. But the thing that really struck me from the meeting was the question Mr. Hamann posed near the end of the time when he asked, "How do you think your parents' divorce has affected your attitude toward relationships and marriage?"

"Most people think about weddings as happy occasions," said Cindi. "But whenever I see a car decorated with 'Just Married' signs or hear the horns of a wedding procession, I'm struck with a feeling of sadness. Sadness for what happened to my family, sadness about the pain the future might hold for those newlyweds, sadness about all the people who've been hurt when their families have been torn apart. I guess I'm pessimistic about marriage. Mine and everyone else's."

"I'll be honest here," Ryan said. "Seeing what's happened in my family has convinced me I never want to get married. Someday, when I'm older, if I fall in love, I'd move in with a girl. If you're not married, you don't have to involve lawyers and go through the pain of a divorce when you break up. Maybe that's being cynical. But that's the way I feel."

I felt I had to say something. "In my case, what my parents went through made me even more committed to my future marriage. I'm determined not to make the same mistake. So I want to be very careful about who

143

I marry and I'll do whatever it takes to make the relationship work because I know how much breaking up can hurt people." When I finished I glanced over at Jennifer, but she was staring at the floor and didn't look up.

Brad said, "I think my parents' divorce hurt me because I never got to see commitment in a relationship; I never saw two people work out a difference or a problem. I've dated a few girls, but as soon as there was any disagreement or problem, I'd drop 'em. It'd be some little thing, but I'd be gone. I don't think the girls ever understood what was going on. I didn't realize it myself until just recently."

"As far as marriage goes," Angela said, "I think I'm gonna be careful before I make any commitment. But my dating relationships have also been affected. I'm careful not to make myself too vulnerable. I'm afraid of getting hurt by another man like I was hurt by my dad. When I date someone, he has to really show that he cares about me because I haven't had much of that from my dad."

When no one else said anything for a time, Mr. Hamann spoke up. "The reason I asked this question was because I think the area of relationships is where my parents' divorce has affected me the most. For a long time, during high school and most of college, I had a retarded view of dating. I overcompensated by wanting to be too committed. I wanted to play married, to spend every possible moment with whatever girl I was dating, to see her as sort of an exclusive friend who was totally involved in my life. I'd seen what a lack of commitment had done in my family and I wanted to keep that from happening in my relationships. So I'd commit myself to a girl and I'd expect her to do the same with me. Of course, that created a lot of problems for the girls I dated. I didn't see that I was smothering them by coming on with such intense commitment.

"On the other hand, I've talked with many people from divorced families who say they shy away from commitment. They reacted just the opposite from me. But both reactions can cause problems.

"I don't want to get too personal, or embarrass anyone. But you ought to know that your parents' divorce can affect your attitude toward sexual behavior, too. Some people look at their parents' situation, especially if one of their parents is playing the field before or after the divorce, and they think, 'If my mom or my dad can do that, then what's stopping me?' And they dump whatever sexual values or restraints they might have had.

"I've seen too many cases, especially with girls who feel rejected by their fathers, where a person will try desperately to replace the lost relationship with another kind of intimate relationship. They get sexually involved with a boyfriend or even a number of boyfriends before they learn that isn't the problem. Some never learn. Maybe we'll talk about this more later, but I wanted to at least bring the subject up because I think it's important for all of us to realize that our parents' divorces will affect our relationships. And if we realize that, maybe we can minimize the damage it'll do."

On the drive back to her house after the meeting, I asked Jennifer what she thought was the most helpful part of the meeting.

"I don't know," she said. "I didn't think about it that way."

"Well, I thought the last thing Mr. Hamann said was

pretty thought provoking. Didn't you?"

"I guess so," she replied noncommittally. "What do you mean exactly?"

"That you need to understand how your parents' divorce affects your own relationships."

"Yeah, I think that's true," she said cautiously.

I plowed right ahead with my thought. "It made me think about our relationship. How I don't want to be afraid to make a commitment and get close to you, but I don't want to smother you by being too committed either. My parents' divorce has already disrupted so much of my life, I want to be very careful to make certain it doesn't disrupt the most wonderful thing that ever happened to me. I know I've said it before, but I'll say it again: I don't ever want to hurt you, Jennifer."

She smiled at me and leaned her head against my shoulder. We were both quiet and thinking our own thoughts until we reached Jennifer's house.

I turned off the engine, and we sat for a few moments before I said, "I've been thinking about some of the things I read in those books, and about what Mr. Hamann said about girls sometimes looking for sexual intimacy from guys to try to find the acceptance they aren't getting anymore from their fathers. What do you think about that?"

Jennifer sat up slowly and looked at me. "What do you mean?"

"I was mostly thinking about Melissa and how I'd hate to see that happen to her. What do you think I could do to help her?"

Jennifer leaned her head back against my shoulder. "I'm not sure. But I think you're sweet to be concerned about her."

"I don't know what I'd do if I learned she was sexually involved with some guy. I don't want her to get messed up. Should I talk to her? Tell her what Mr. Hamann said, or what?"

"She doesn't even have a boyfriend yet, Matt. I don't think she needs a lecture."

"You're probably right," I said. But I kept thinking about Melissa until I felt Jennifer lean toward me and gently kiss my ear.

"I think you're sweet to be concerned about her." She brushed her lips along my cheek and asked, "But can I get you to stop worrying about your little sister for a few minutes?"

"Mmmm. I doubt it," I said teasingly.

Jennnifer's lips met mine, and she gave me a long kiss. When she finally pulled back she smiled and said, "I think Melissa will be just fine."

"Melissa who?"

Jennifer laughed and I pulled her against me. For the next few minutes, I couldn't have thought of anything but Jennifer if I'd have tried. Which I didn't.

I think we were both getting pretty worked up when Jennifer leaned away and said, "I'd better go in."

She sounded reluctant. If I'd said, "Don't," I think she would have stayed. I wanted her to stay; I was certain she felt the same passion I felt. But I didn't want to push. So while my hormones were screaming "NO!" my lips said, "OK." And sixty seconds later we both got out of the car.

Climbing the steps to her front porch I said, "I'm glad you talked me into going to the meetings."

"Me, too, Matt. But I don't know if I'd be going without you, either."

I shook my head. "I think I could relate to just about everything we talked about tonight. Except maybe the question about step-parents. Fortunately, I haven't had to worry about that yet."

"But you will someday," Jennifer said. "Sooner or later."

I'd have picked "later." But it wasn't my choice.

CHAPTER

14

Moving was easier than I thought it would be. And harder.

It was easier in the sense that an entire houseful of furniture can be loaded on a truck in a matter of hours. We hadn't moved since I was old enough to remember, so I'd never imagined what it was like to see all your worldly possessions stacked up in one visible pile.

But it was hard trudging slowly through the house, empty of everything but memories. The bare walls were a screen on which the projector of my mind flashed a film of my life's highlights. I saw scuff marks I'd never seen on the floors before.

There was a crack I'd never noticed in the frame on my bedroom closet door—but it wasn't my bedroom anymore. It wasn't my home. Just an empty house that would hold no meaning for its next occupants, until they gave it meaning.

Mom, Melissa, Mark and I walked through the house together one last time. No one said anything. But I'm sure we shared the same sadness. Mom was the last one out, locking the door and the house behind us.

Driving away for the last time, I looked back and saw the well-worn driveway and the broken backboard behind the house. I'd never gotten around to putting up the new one. I would have left it for the next owners, but Mom insisted that since it was a Christmas present, we'd load it on the truck.

I still hadn't gotten used to the feel of our new townhouse when Dad called one afternoon the next week and asked if the two of us could get together for a little while that evening.

"I guess so," I said without enthusiasm. The emotion of the move had prompted a new wave of resentment. "What's up?"

"I'll tell you when I see you. Seven-thirty?"

"OK," I agreed.

"Want a Coke or something? We could stop at a Seven-Eleven store and grab a Big Gulp or something," Dad said as we entered the main road in front of our new subdivision.

"Sure."

We got our drinks and climbed back into the car before Dad got to the point of our meeting. "I don't know the best way to say this, Matt. . . ."

This sounds painfully familiar.

"I wanted you to be the first person to know that Gwynn and I have decided we want to get married."

I almost choked on a swallow of Mountain Dew. After a few awkward seconds of shocked silence, I managed one word: "When?"

"Two weeks from tomorrow. The last Saturday of March." I almost snapped at him, *Why? Do you have to get married?* But I bit my tongue and maintained a shocked silence.

Dad went on. "I wanted you to know right away because you're my oldest son. But also because I have a special request of you." He paused and waited for me to look at him.

When I finally did, he said, "I'd like you to do me the honor of standing as my best man."

I didn't hear him right. I couldn't have.

"I don't want you to give me an answer tonight, Matt. Take a few days to think about it. I can see this comes as big surprise. And I guess it does seem kinda sudden to you. But it's been almost a year since your mom and I separated."

It doesn't matter if it's been ten years. "I don't know. . . ."

"Don't try to give me any answer now, Matt. Just think about it. It'd mean a lot to me. There's no one I'd rather have beside me. And while I know I've hurt you kids and your mom, I still want to be your father. I still am your father. I still want to share my life with you. And this is an important part of my life. So just promise me you'll think about it for a couple of days before you give me an answer. OK?"

I nodded. "OK."

I thought about it all right; I couldn't get it out of my mind for the next couple of days. I didn't say anything to Mom even though she'd have to know eventually.

Jennifer and I had a date Saturday night. So of course I told her.

"Are you going to do it?" she asked.

"I don't see how I can. It'd be like condoning everything he's done to Mom. To all of us."

"Not necessarily."

151

I looked at Jennifer incredulously. "You think I should do it?"

"I don't know," she replied. "I just think there's a lot to consider."

"Like what?!"

"Like he's still your father. And he's saying he wants you to still be a big part of his life. That's more important than you know, Matt. Until you don't have it anymore."

I knew she was talking from experience. "But I can't condone what he's doing!" I insisted.

"What if you just attended the wedding? Do you feel like that would be condoning it?"

"That's different . . . I guess. Uh, I don't know."

"Well," Jennifer said, "let me ask this. Do you think your father knows now how you feel about his leaving your mom, taking up with Gwynn, and planning to get remarried?"

"Sure. He knows I'm hurt. He knows I think the whole idea stinks. He knows I think what he did was a big sin. I haven't said all that in so many words, but he has to know how I feel."

"He knows how strongly you feel those things, right?"

"I'm sure he does."

"Then would going to his wedding, or even being his best man change any of that? Would it really say to him that you changed your opinion?"

"I guess not. He'd still know how I really felt. But . . . ," I looked at Jennifer. "So you think I should do it?"

She shook her head. "I didn't say that. I don't know. You have to be the one to decide. I just think you need to be careful not to burn any bridges you don't have to burn. Anything you can do to preserve or rebuild your relationship can be important."

She had a good point. My relationship with Dad had been strained to the limit over the last year. I didn't want to do it any more damage. Yet . . . "What about my mom? If I do this for Dad, what does it say to Mom? I'd feel worse than Judas!"

"Could you talk to her?"

"I don't even think she knows Dad's getting married. And I don't want to be the one to tell her!"

"I'm sorry, Matt." She tucked her arm through mine and leaned against my shoulder. "It's a tough decision."

"Yeah." It made me angry to have to make it. Sunday, right after the worship service at church, I bumped into Gary Matthews in the hall. "You and I ought to get together," he said. "We haven't had a good long talk since that breakfast at McDonald's. I'd like to know what's up with you."

I needed another perspective. "You got five minutes right now, Gary?"

"Sure," he said. "Let's just step into my office."

So I quickly summarized my dilemma, including some of Jennifer's insights. He listened thoughfully. "Which way are you leaning?" he asked when I had finished.

"I don't know. I certainly don't want to hurt Mom, or make her feel I'm condoning what Dad's done. But I don't want to build any more walls between Dad and me either."

Gary thought for a minute. "I think you're right to be concerned about your mom's reaction. In some ways this is just between you and your dad, but you have to be sensitive to her feelings. And she has to know your thinking. Whatever you decide, probably before you decide, you need to talk to her."

"I know," I admitted. I'd pretty much come to that conclusion myself.

"I understand that you don't want your dad to think you're condoning everything either. But I think your decision could carry other messages you need to think about."

I didn't understand what Gary was getting at. "Like what?"

"Saying 'yes' could also say to your dad that you still love him. It could say to him that you want to work at maintaining your relationship and that your relationship with him is more important than anything he or you could ever do to strain it. Saying 'no' might send an opposite message."

"I want him to know I still love him. I want to maintain our relationship. But I have a hard time condoning and forgiving what he did."

"Condoning and forgiving are two different things, Matt. You don't have to condone something to forgive someone. In fact, in forgiving something you're acknowledging that there's a wrong to forgive."

"Yeah. I guess. I'm just not sure I'm ready to forgive him. I know I ought to; he's my father. But when I think about what he did to Mom, to our family, I don't feel very forgiving."

Gary nodded. "That's understandable. And I don't want to tell you what you ought to do. You have to decide that for yourself. For your mom. And your dad. But sometimes feelings—feelings like forgiveness— only come after we do something forgiving."

That evening, after Melissa and Mark had gone to bed, I walked into the kitchen where Mom was emptying the dishwasher. Leaning against the kitchen cabinets, I said, "Mom, I've got something I need to talk to you about."

She turned around. "Is this about your father?"

"Yes, I—"

"I know about the marriage, Matt. He called this afternoon to tell me." I tried to gauge the pain in her eyes, but she turned back around and began stacking Tupperware tumblers on the counter.

At least I don't have to be the one to tell her. A few seconds passed before I said, "That's only part of it."

"I know," she said. "He told me what he asked you." She put the tumblers on their shelf in the cupboard and began emptying the silverware basket. "He's hoping for an answer in the next couple of days." She still didn't turn back around. "Do you know what you're going to do?"

"I don't know. That's why I wanted to talk to you."

"I think what you do should be between you and your dad, Matt." She closed the silverware drawer, put the basket back in place, and closed the dishwasher door.

"But I don't want to hurt you."

She turned around and I could clearly read the depth of her hurt through the transparent sorrow in her face. "A person can only be hurt so much," she said.

"But I wouldn't want you to think I'm taking Dad's side. . . ."

"I know that, Matt," she said, patting my arm. "You've been very supportive."

"I also don't want Dad to feel I'm condoning what he's done to you. To the whole family."

"He knows you better than that, Matt. When he called today, he said he'd never ask you to approve of what he did. I'm sure he can't even condone it himself. He knows what he did was wrong. He knows he hurt all of us. He wants us to forgive him."

"How can I forgive him? Do you forgive him?"

"I'm trying to," she said. "It's hard. It'd be a lot easier if forgiveness would wipe out the past, but it doesn't. Sometimes the best forgiveness can do is give us a new place to start.

"That's why I think you should go to your father's wedding. And you should stand up there with him. It'll give you a new place to start. You need that. He's still your father. And he's always going to be your father."

I watched her face as she said those words. *Did she really mean it?* "How can you be so understanding, Mom? Aren't you bitter?"

She gave me small smile that only intensified the sadness on her face and in her eyes. "Sure, I'm bitter. Some days I feel like there's nothing inside me but a cistern of bitterness. And a lot of days I don't think I understand any of what's happened to us. But I have to trust that God is there, helping me to go beyond the bitterness."

When I remained silent, she patted my arm again. "Tell your father you'll do it. He needs you. And if you can't bring yourself to do it for him, do it for yourself, Matt. You need him, too."

Then she walked past me and out of the kitchen. And I knew she meant what she'd said.

Weddings should be happy celebrations of new beginnings. But when one of your parents gets remarried, it's also the end of something. Maybe the end of any last remnants of hope that it can all be right again someday.

But I did it. At a small, private ceremony at Gwynn's

parents' home, I stood beside my father and listened to him pledge his undying love for a woman I didn't know. I watched him kiss his new bride after the minister pronounced them man and wife. I smiled and shook hands when I was introduced to the guests at the reception. And none of it was easy.

Finally it was time to take Melissa and Mark home. Dad walked us to the car. He kissed Melissa and Mark good-bye and promised to call as soon as he and Gwynn got back from a week in Acapulco. Then he walked around the car to the driver's side with me.

He shook my hand. And then he gave me a big hug. When I hugged him back I felt a bond, a warmth I hadn't felt between us for a long time. "It means a lot to me that you came today," he said after he released me from the embrace. "Thank you, Matt."

"You're welcome, Dad." That was all I could bring myself to say. But I really meant it. And that surprised me a little.

I was glad I'd promised to call Jennifer as soon as we got home. It meant I had an excuse to leave the room as Mark excitedly filled Mom in on the details.

"Tell me about it," Jennifer said.

So I gave her the details of the ceremony and my own reactions.

"Sounds like an emotionally exhausting evening," she observed.

"Yeah," I admitted. "But I made it. And I guess I'm glad I did it." I told her about my feelings when I said good-bye to Dad.

We talked a little more and made plans for me to come to her house the next afternoon. Then we said our good-byes.

"Matt?" she said, just as I was starting to hang up.

"Yeah?"

"I'm glad it went so well. I was praying for you tonight."

"Thanks," I replied. "I think it helped."

After I'd hung up, I thought about Jennifer. About her praying for me. I knew Mom had been been praying for me. And so had Gary Matthews, he'd called last night to tell me he would.

I can't say I had been conscious of their prayers while I'd been at the wedding. But as I thought about it now, I appreciated them. They must have helped.

But realizing that brought a wave of guilt. While Mom and Jennifer and Gary had prayed for me, I hadn't bothered to pray myself. I hadn't prayed a real, honest prayer since I'd challenged God to do something to show he really cared.

A wave of sudden anger washed over the guilt. If God had answered their prayers today, where was he when I'd begged him to save my parents' marriage, when I'd prayed that he'd at least do something, anything to prove his concern and help me. *All I've gotten is silence*, I thought angrily. *That's why I haven't prayed a real, honest prayer in months. Not since before Jennifer took me to that first discussion group.* . . .

Suddenly, I paused. I'd never thought about those two things in conjunction before. My prayer for help and the discussion group. It was like a light came on and I could begin to see a connection. Part of my mind said *It was just a coincidence*. Another part said, *There are no coincidences*. My heart said, *It doesn't matter. If there are coincidences, God could certainly use them.*

And I realized God had used those discussion groups to show me my feelings, to help me understand what I was going through. From the group I'd learned about books to read, books that had helped tremendously.

As that truth dawned, I realized God *had* answered my prayer. And the moment I admitted that, it was like the sun came up after a long, cold winter night and I could see everything in a fresh new light. Not only was there the discussion group, there was Gary Matthews and his support. There was Mom and her incredible strength through the past few months. And of course there was Jennifer.

But, reasoned the questioning part of my mind, *I met Jennifer back before my parents even split up.* With that thought, I realized a more wonderful truth. Months before I'd prayed my desperate prayer, God had been working on an answer. Jennifer was part of the answer. I would never have survived without Jennifer—there was no denying that.

As one revelation after another hit me, there was no denying God either. After months of absence, or at least of hibernation, my faith was coming awake and alive. I believed again.

I knew beyond any shadow of doubt not only that God still cared about me, but that Jennifer was a very special part of my life. And I knew I needed to talk to her about it as soon as I could.

Jennifer greeted me at her front door with a big hug and kiss. "I checked a couple of videos out of the library," she said. "Wanna watch *Back to the Future*?"

"Sure," I said. "I haven't seen it for a couple of years."

"Great! Let's make some popcorn first."

I followed her into the kitchen. "Where's your mom?" I asked.

"She took Valerie and went to visit a friend for the day. I've been all alone since nine this morning."

"Well, you've got some wonderful company now."

"Oh, yeah? I didn't hear any doorbell."

I made a face and she laughed. I flicked a popcorn seed at her and she laughed again.

While we waited for the corn to pop, I told her about the insight I'd had the night before. About how I could see the ways God used the discussion group to really help me and how that "just happened" to come up right after I'd been praying for some help, some sign from God.

Jennifer nodded. "I thought about that at the time," she said. "I even mentioned it to you a couple of times."

"You did?"

She grinned and nodded again. "Guess that shows how much you listen to me."

I didn't remember any conversation like that. "What it shows is you can't tell anyone anything unless they're ready to hear it." I told her about the other ways I now could see God had been working: through the stuff I read on divorce; through Gary and Mom; and especially through her. I told her how I now realized that God brought her into my life even before I knew how much I needed her.

"I don't know what I'd have done this past year without you. You knew what I was going through. You listened to me. You helped me understand myself. You've been perfect for me.

"Now that I feel close to God for the first time in at least ten months, I feel closer than ever to you." I could see a tear trickling down Jennifer's cheek as I talked. I pulled her to me. "I love you so much. Even more now that I understand how God brought us together."

"I love you, too, Matt," she said. And we stood there holding each other until Jennifer finally said, "I think the popcorn's ready."

We cuddled up on the family room sofa with our popcorn and soda. And as Michael J. Fox journeyed back in time, I noticed a number of wonderful lines I'd missed the first three times I'd seen it; my measure of a great movie.

When the time machine finally blasted off for the future at the end of the movie, and the credits began to roll, I couldn't help thinking about how the character Marty had altered his own fate when he interfered with his parents' "destiny." It made me think of my own parents and my own life.

As the machine rewound the tape, I pulled Jennifer close until her head rested on my shoulder. "Do you think some people are just meant for each other?" I asked.

"You mean like Marty's parents?"

I laughed. "I hope not exactly like Marty's parents. But they did start me thinking. Do you think God has one specific partner in mind for each person to meet, fall in love with, and marry?"

"I don't know . . . maybe sometimes," Jennifer replied. "I didn't realize that was such a heavy philosophical movie. What do you think?"

"Maybe," I said. But as I looked down into Jennifer's face I felt pretty sure I knew the answer. At least for me.

I thought about saying so right then and there. But I decided I wanted to choose my words carefully. I wanted the time and the place to be just right.

CHAPTER
15

The acceptance letters came only two days apart during the first week in April. First from the state university with the great computer science department. Then from the Christian liberal arts college with the reputation for a good journalism program. They each asked for a special pre-registration fee to reserve a spot for me in the fall.

Decision time. And I wasn't any closer to choosing between a career in computers or one in journalism. I talked through the pros and cons with Mom, with Gary Matthews, and of course with Jennifer.

The state university was only a couple of hours away. I could come home more and see Jennifer more often; she was going to get a job next year to earn enough to go to school the following year. The university would be cheaper. And I did love computers.

But I knew the Christian college would challenge me to grow spiritually as well as intellectually. The catalog talked a lot about the importance of integrating faith and learning. And I still had a lot of interest in a possible career in journalism.

"What it really boils down to," I told Jennifer, "is which career direction I go. I've prayed about it, but I don't feel ready to make that decision yet.

"Another thing that's bothering me is that, always before when I've had big decisions to make, I've had my dad to talk to. And the last few days I've felt the resentment creeping back in. I resent the fact that I'm facing one of the biggest decisions of my life and he's not there for me."

"You could always go over and see him. It's not like he's clear across the country."

"I know. But he's not here for me in the same way. I don't feel like I know him that well anymore. Or that he really knows me, either. At least not in the same way you know someone you live with every day."

"He lived with you for seventeen years, Matt. He probably knows you better than you think. I say you ought to talk to him."

So I did. I called him at his office and asked if I could come by that night to talk. He invited me for supper. Gwynn's lasagna was good, but I didn't feel very comfortable talking about my decision during the meal. She must have sensed it because after we finished eating, she said, "Why don't you two go out on the porch and talk? I can clean up in here."

That's where I told Dad about the two acceptance letters and the choice I needed to make. He asked me if I'd made a list of the pros and cons either way. I told him what I'd come up with and he added a couple of other thoughts, but nothing that tipped the balance. He went into the house and returned with a pencil and some paper and asked me to make a list of the three most positive and memorable achievements I remembered from ages six to nine. He told me to do the same thing from ages ten to twelve, thirteen to fifteen, and sixteen to seventeen.

"I don't see how this is going to help," I said.

"Just do it," he said. "I'll explain when you're done."

When I finished, he had me read him the list. "Sometimes you can see a pattern of activities or kinds of activities that a person consistently enjoys and is good at," he explained. "Some people seem more mechanical or thing-oriented while others relate more to people. Some are more leaders than followers. And so on. Sometimes a pattern shows up that people didn't realize was there. When that happens you have another factor to help in the decision process."

"Do you see a pattern?" I asked as he read over what I'd written.

"Two of them," he said, grinning. "You seem to find a lot of satisfaction and enjoyment from working with computers and from doing things related to writing."

I couldn't help laughing. "Great! So which do I choose?"

"I don't think you should choose either."

"But I have to choose one school or the other. I can't go to both."

Dad shook his head. "I meant don't choose a career. At least not yet. You've got lots of time to decide. Most college students change their majors at least once. Some change it several times. You shouldn't feel pressured to make any decision before you're ready."

"But that decision would determine which school—"

"You're putting the cart before the horse, Matt. You're saying you can only decide on the school if you decide on a career. Then you're saying you have to at least make a tentative decision on a career, which you don't feel ready to make. But neither of these two statements is true. It's not even true that you can't go to both schools. Lots of people go to two or more colleges before they graduate."

"So what are you saying?"

"That you have another very good option. Choose the school you think would be better for you apart from those two majors. Take your general requirements and some sample courses in journalism and computer science for two years. If you decide to stay, fine. And if you decide the other school has what you need, you can always transfer."

What Dad said made so much sense, that by the time I had to leave, I felt very glad I'd come. "Thanks a lot for the input, Dad," I said as we said our good-byes.

"You still have to decide where to start."

"But your idea takes a lot of pressure off the decision. It would keep my options open. At least for another two years." I felt a sense of relief already.

Dad smiled. "Glad I could help. Just remember I'm here if you need me."

"I could use a little help next Saturday."

"Sure," he said. "With what?"

"I've got this Christmas present I'd like to mount on the garage of our townhouse. And when that's done I need someone to whip in a game of 'Horse' "

Dad grinned and clapped me on the shoulder. "I'll be glad to help put up the backboard. But you'll have to find somebody else to beat. After I get done whippin' you, of course."

I walked out of Dad's front door laughing.

The next day I called Jennifer and told her about my talk with Dad. "Sounds like good advice to me," she said. "So which school is it gonna be?"

"I don't know for sure. State would be cheaper. And closer. I could come home more often to see you. But a smaller school would have a warmer, more personal atmosphere. And there'd be the spiritual dimension. Maybe I'd want to transfer to state eventually anyway. I'd have the experience of both.

"Who knows? In two years, if I transferred to state, tuition would be cheaper, maybe we'd be ready to make some decisions. If you were going to school there, they have university housing, we might even be able to afford to get married. . . ."

I hadn't meant to say anything like that. Certainly not over the phone. It just slipped out. Probably because I'd been thinking about the idea so much.

Jennifer didn't respond.

"Anything could happen, right?" I prodded.

Again silence. I heard her take a deep breath before she said, "Matt, I don't want you to take this wrong. OK?"

"OK. What?"

"I don't think you should make any big life decision about school or career on account of me. OK?"

"What do you mean?" I asked, wanting some sort of reassurance that the words didn't mean anything serious. That in an unselfish manner she was telling me to make the decision I thought best for me, and that she, and we, would be fine.

"It's not something I want to talk about over the telephone. Can we talk about it when you come over tomorrow?"

"OK," I said.

But it wasn't OK. I didn't sleep all night. I kept telling myself everything was going to be all right. It had to be!

I tossed and turned and thought about Jennifer. About our relationship. About the first time I ever saw her and wondered who she was. About driving her home and asking her out. About that first date when I knew I was falling for her.

I thought about all those times she'd been there when I needed to talk, when I'd call her on the phone and tell her what was going on with Mom and Dad. Or when we'd sit in the car talking and she'd lay her head on my shoulder, hold my hand, and let me pour out my own feelings. How she'd prodded me to open up, first with her and then with the people in the divorce group at her school.

I thought about the comforting feel of her head against my shoulder, her hair under my cheek as I leaned my head against hers. I remembered the warmth of her lips, the softness of her body pressed against me when I'd held her in my arms.

And as I thought about Jennifer, about us, I searched my memory for some clue, some indication of what could be bothering her. I could find nothing. Our relationship was growing—deeper and better.

This can't be that serious, I told myself. *You're making too much out of this.* But I couldn't believe my own assurances. Something felt very wrong. And the longer I lay awake wondering about it, the more wrong it felt.

Neither of us said much the next evening until we'd pulled into McDougals and ordered our usuals. A large chocolate malt for me and a Diet 7-Up for Jennifer.

Even before the carhop brought our order, Jennifer said, "I've been thinking a lot today about what I started to say last night."

"Me, too," I said. "What did you mean you didn't think I should make any big decision on account of you?"

"I meant that I didn't think I should be a factor in whatever decision you make. You need to decide what's best for you."

I turned and looked at her. She was staring out the front windshield when I said, "I've been thinking you were what's best for me, Jennifer. You happen to be a pretty big factor in my life. I don't want to make any decision without considering you. Not now. Not ever."

She turned and looked at me. "Maybe you should. Maybe we're getting too serious, Matt. Maybe we need to back off and give each other some room."

Just like that it hit me, and I was fighting for breath in a sudden tidal wave of emotions. I was fighting for survival. Ours. My own.

"Wait a minute." I felt as if I was begging for time. Time to think. To understand. To breathe. "We're both almost eighteen. A lot of people start to get serious at our age. We love each other. I love you. I thought you loved me."

"I thought . . . I think I love you, Matt. It's just that I've begun to feel more and more uneasy about our relationship lately."

"What do you mean by that?" This couldn't be happening; this was the girl God brought into my life even before I knew how much I needed her. "The only fight we ever had was when I drove off and left you in the church parking lot that time. And that shouldn't even count because we weren't even going together then. We make a great couple, everyone who knows us thinks so. Even your mom is beginning to like me. And you're perfect for—"

"That's . . . that's part of the problem," she said, interrupting me.

"What is?"

I watched her gnawing on her lower lip for several seconds before she took a deep breath, turned to look at me, and said, "You think I'm perfect. But I'm not. I'm far from it. And it's time you knew it."

"Now what are you saying?"

"I guess I'm saying it's time you really knew me."

"I do know you," I protested. "I know you well enough to know I love you."

She shook her head sadly and turned to stare out the front windshield. Finally she said, "I know you pretty well, too —what you feel, what you've been through, especially in this past year. But I don't think you know me at all. You haven't—"

"I know—"

"Let me finish," she said. "You don't know me like I know you because we've spent a lot more time talking about you and what you've been going through."

The truth of that stabbed deep. "I'm sorry," I said. "I should have listened more. I want to listen, to understand."

"I don't really blame you," she assured me. "The things you've been struggling with are happening right now. They're immediate, so they're easier for you to talk about. Your deepest hurt is so close to the surface it almost has to come out. While mine is buried so deep I've never told a soul about it."

"Can you tell me now?" I asked uncertainly. I wanted to know— and yet I didn't want to know.

She didn't look at me; she just stared straight ahead. "Ever since my dad left us I've had problems relating to men, to guys. I remember my mom's bitterness right after the divorce. 'Men are only interested in one thing!' she said. 'They'll love you as long as they get what they want, until something they think looks better comes along. So you have to be careful with men. You can't trust 'em.'"

"You told me that a long time ago," I said. It didn't surprise me that would keep her from relating to guys.

"But I didn't tell you . . . well, everything. I didn't tell you what happened during junior high school. Looking back I can see I was trying to fill the hole my dad left in my life. I so needed his love that I was desperate for any male attention and affirmation. And since my mother kept warning me that men were only interested in one thing, I figured that was the one way to get the positive assurance I needed.

"I started flirting with a couple of boys in my seventh grade homeroom. I liked Paul better than I did John, but John asked me out first. So I went with him to the first away basketball game of the year. On the way home we sat in the back of the bus and necked. I liked it. And John evidently did, too, because he asked me to go with him to the next game and the next. We became regular fixtures in the back of the bus.

"John moved away right after Christmas, and I was devastated. But the first day of school after the holidays, Paul asked me to go to the next game with him. We sat in the back of the bus and took right up where John and I'd left off.

"Paul and I didn't hit it off all that well. We only went out together two or three games. But evidently my back-of-the-bus behavior hadn't gone unnoticed.

Three or four other guys started asking me out to dances, parties, or whatever was going on at school.

"The attention felt good. And so did the making out. It started out tame enough. Hugging and kissing on the back of the bus or in the corner during a party. But before long, there was a little petting. Then a lot of petting. I realized I was getting a reputation around school. But it seemed like a small price to pay for all the attention I got. It felt good to know that guys wanted me."

I wanted to tell Jennifer to stop, that she didn't have to tell me all this. When she paused I said, "This doesn't change anything as far as I'm concerned. It's past. I think—"

"There's more you need to hear," she said, stopping me. "At least, there's more I need to say." So I waited for her to go on.

"In eighth grade I started dating a high school football player. I was the envy of every junior high girl I knew. I couldn't believe he wanted to date me. I'd have done anything to keep his interest. And, uh . . . I did."

I don't want to hear this! I thought. But Jennifer went on, haltingly.

"We . . . started to have sex. And a couple of months later I missed my period. When I told my boyfriend after the second month, I learned that the rest of Mom's warning was true, too.

"The jerk dropped me on the spot. Said it was my problem and probably wasn't his baby anyway. I wanted to die. But instead, the baby did. I had a miscarriage about the tenth week. Nobody else ever knew. Nobody else ever needed to know. Until now."

My mind was reeling with horrible images of Jennifer making out in the back of a bus, groping around in the backseat of a car, and in bed with some guy I suddenly wanted to slug.

I didn't want to believe it. But the look on Jennifer's face left no doubts. I could feel a knot tightening in my gut.

"You're a different person now," I finally said, wanting to believe my own words. I thought I knew Jennifer, but now I felt uncertain. I took a deep breath, swallowed the hurt and said, "I love you, Jennifer." I knew that for sure. What I said next I at least wanted to believe. "What happened back then doesn't have to come between us. It doesn't need to affect us at all."

Jennifer sighed. "But it does. Don't you see, Matt? I've never had a healthy, normal dating relationship with a guy."

"Except for me."

She went right on. "I spent two years in junior high giving guys what I thought they wanted just so I could feel loved and desirable. When I moved before ninth grade it gave me a chance to start over without the old reputation. Some of my new friends invited me to their church where I learned about God's love and eventually asked his forgiveness."

"Which makes you a different person, a new person," I pointed out.

"Sure," she admitted. "But forgiveness doesn't automatically wipe out the past, at least not the effects of the past. For more than three years after I got pregnant, I couldn't trust any guy enough to date him more than a couple of times." She turned and looked at me as a tear trickled out of her eye and down her cheek.

"Until I met you, Matt."

"OK," I said. "But our relationship hasn't been like those others, has it?"

"I told myself all along it was different, but . . ."

"It is different, Jennifer."

"You've never pressured me physically. No. That's the only reason I kept going out with you after the first couple of times, the only reason I let myself care."

I thought of all the times I'd kissed her, all the times we stopped before my body and my emotions wanted to stop. And I felt a sudden gratitude that I hadn't done anything that would have ruined our relationship. "So you have to admit our relationship is different."

"In one way, yes," she admitted. "But in another sense it's not different at all."

She'd lost me. "I don't understand."

"I don't know if I can put the feeling into words," she said. "But I'll try. You haven't wanted or needed me just for my body. But you have wanted and needed me for support and encouragement because of all you've been going through this past year. You've used me to—"

"Wait a minute. What do you mean I 'used' you?"

I didn't like what she was saying. "I don't mean that to sound so negative, Matt. I don't mean you took advantage of me, or that you were only concerned about yourself."

"I love you, Jennifer. Don't you believe that?"

"Of course, I do. And I've enjoyed being needed the way you've needed me to talk with and to listen. . . ."

"Then I really don't understand what you're saying."

She sighed and I waited, trying to understand in the silence what she was trying to tell me. Finally she turned to me again and said, "Your needing me has made me feel good and worthwhile, much the same way I felt in those junior high relationships."

"I still don't understand. . . ."

"For a long time I didn't either. I convinced myself that I must love you. But maybe . . . maybe I just love that feeling of being wanted and needed by a man because I missed out on that when my daddy left us. Whatever the reason, I think I need time and space to figure it all out."

Time and space? Those were the same words Dad used when he said he was leaving. I had a sick feeling about where this was leading, but I had to ask, "What does that mean?"

"I guess," said Jennifer, "it means I think it might be best if we quit seeing each other."

No! This isn't happening! I felt like a drowning man who desperately needed a breath of air, of hope.

"Why can't we keep dating and work together to try to figure out whether our love is real? We can help each other detect the ways our parents' divorces have affected us."

Jennifer shook her head. "The more time we spend together, the more our emotions complicate things. It'd be just that much harder to break up later. And the longer we go together, the more physical we'd become."

How can this be happening? I thought frantically. *Why haven't I seen or felt something? How could I not have had any clue about what was going on inside Jennifer? Was I that blind? How can she suddenly seem so determined to end our relationship?* I had a thousand questions and no good answers.

Finally I said, "I've spent the last month incredibly happy, thinking that God brought us together because he knew how much I needed you. Are you going to tell me you don't think He wanted us together?" I wasn't above bringing God into this discussion. Anything to make her reconsider.

But she countered, "Maybe God just wanted us together because we needed each other this past year. Maybe he wanted us to learn from this relationship so we could have better relationships in the future."

"Do you really believe that?"

"I don't know, Matt. I really don't know."

"Then don't do this to me, Jennifer!"

"I don't want to hurt you, Matt." As she said that, tears began to roll down her face. "This is hard for me, too. I don't want to break up with you."

"Then don't."

"I have to," she cried. "At least, I think I have to."

We went round and round for another hour. But we didn't get anywhere.

I finally took her home. She was crying and holding tightly to my hand as I walked her to the door. It all seemed so crazy. She said we needed to break up. But we stood on the porch for a long time, our arms around each other, neither one ready to let go. Finally she stepped back and opened the front door.

"Good night, Matt," she whispered as she stepped inside and closed the door between us. I sat in the car in front of her house, watching until the light in her room went off. It seemed like an hour passed after that before the tears finally ran out and I could see to drive home.

I didn't sleep that night. Or the next.

A week passed; the loneliest week of my life. For months I'd talked to Jennifer every day, at least on the phone. Now, with no one to share the little events of my days, I felt cut off. And with each passing day the pain grew worse.

Finally I had to call. Jennifer's mom answered the phone. I asked to speak to Jennifer. A couple of minutes passed before I heard her come on the line. "Hello."

"It's me, Matt."

"I know."

"I need to talk to you. Can I come over and talk?"

"I don't think so."

"Please?"

"Matt, don't make this any harder."

"This is tearing me up, Jennifer. I can't sleep. I can't concentrate in school. I have to talk to you."

"I don't think talking will change anything."

"Please, Jennifer." I was begging now. "For almost a year now I've thought about you every day. You've given me strength. You've made me laugh. You've given me a reason to keep on living when my whole life was coming apart. I can't just forget all that because one night, out of the blue, you tell me you need time to figure out your problems before you can be sure you love me." I paused, but not long enough to give her time to say no before I went on. "I want to give you time and space if you need it, because I love you, Jennifer. I want you to have whatever you need to be happy. If I could just understand . . . if we could talk . . . we can't end a whole year with one conversation. Please, I need to talk to—"

"OK."

I caught my breath. "We can talk?"

"Yes."

"When?"

"Now, if you want."

"I'll be there in thirty minutes." It was more like twenty-two. And it didn't give me long enough to figure out what to say.

We sat together on the porch swing. For a long time neither of us said anything new. We just plowed the same ground over and over.

Then I had an insight. "You say you don't know how to separate your feelings of love from the good feeling of being needed, right?"

Jennifer nodded.

"There's nothing wrong with being needed, Jennifer. Part of any good relationship is fulfilling each other's needs. A man and a woman complement each other. They offset each other's weaknesses. In a marriage, it's all part of two people becoming one."

"But you've got to have strength to do that," she said. "You have to be a healthy, mature person or you'll always want your own needs to be met without being able to meet your partner's needs. I've gotta get myself straightened out and feel good about myself before I can be sure I can love someone else the way I want to.

"Also, I've realized the last few months in talking with you about divorce, going to the divorce discussion group, and reading more on the subject, that I still have a lot to learn about how my parents' divorce has affected me. I wish it didn't. But it does. And your parents' divorce is affecting you in ways you need to realize, too, Matt."

"Like how?"

"Like the way you're ready to start talking about marriage. How much of that is because you're so determined to prove you can make a marriage work and not make the same mistake your father did? How much of your love for me is just your need for someone who understands all the stuff you've been through this past year?"

"I don't know."

"I don't know either, Matt. That's why I think we both need time to find out."

"Why can't we find out together?"

"We've already talked about that, Matt."

That wasn't the end of the discussion, but it might as well have been. Darkness came before I gave up trying.

It's hard to argue with doubts. Maybe all you can do is test them, I don't know. At least that's what Jennifer was set on doing.

"Can I at least call?" I asked.

"It'll just make it harder," she said.

"Jennifer. . . ."

"I need to go in, Matt. It's getting late." She leaned over and kissed me quickly on the cheek. "I'm sorry," she said as she stood and walked across the porch toward the front door.

"Good night," I called after her.

Before she went in she turned to face me. "Good-bye, Matt," she said softly. And she was gone.

Graduation came and went. But as important a milestone as it was, I found myself thinking about Jennifer as I walked across the stage to receive my diploma. I wished she were there to share that with me, as she'd shared so many other things over the preceding year.

I went to church every Sunday the rest of the spring and summer. It was the one place I could see Jennifer. Sometimes she'd smile at me across the sanctuary and my hopes would soar. Three or four times I asked if I could call her at home. My hopes shattered in pain each time she said no.

We talked for a few minutes after church a couple of times. Around the first of July, I asked her how her summer was going. And when she asked me if I'd made up my mind about school yet, I told her my decision.

"When does school start?" she asked.

"Freshman orientation is the last week of August. I leave the twenty-third and probably won't be back home again until at least Thanksgiving, maybe Christmas. Eight hundred miles is too far to come home for just a weekend." I grinned, "I'll probably get unbelievably homesick."

She smiled. "You'll be fine, Matt. I think you made the right decision."

"Did you?"

She shrugged. "Too early to tell. I think so." Then her ride was leaving. And as I watched her go, it felt as if someone was ripping open a freshly sutured wound in my soul.

Mom, Melissa, and Mark drove me to the airport on the twenty-third. Dad met us at the check-in counter. I checked two suitcases and a couple of small boxes. Mom had promised to ship more of my things when I decided how much I really needed.

We walked to the gate as a family. Dad gave me a big hug. I picked Mark up and held him at my eye level. "You take care of Mom and Melissa, OK, kid?"

He promised. I kissed Melissa and then Mom.

While Mom squeezed me tight she asked, "You think someone who's considering a career in journalism could manage to write home every week or so?"

"I don't know," I said. "I think a lot of reporters have to call in their stories. Collect."

Mom laughed. "That'd be OK, too. Take care of yourself, Matt. Get plenty of rest. And eat right. The first semester of school there's a lot of stress if—"

"Mom! I promise to eat and sleep every day. OK?" She nodded and kissed me again on the cheek as I added, "How about you? You sure you're going to be OK?"

"Don't worry about anything here at home," she said. "Just concentrate on those books. We'll all be fine. We'll miss you, but we'll be fine."

A year before I couldn't have believed her. But my mother had found a strength I didn't know she had in her. Her marriage had come apart. She'd gone back to work. She'd moved. She'd started life over. And, with God's help, she really was going to survive.

I said one more round of good-byes and headed through the door and out to the plane. From my window seat I could see my entire family waving from the terminal—Mom, and on the other side of Melissa and Mark, Dad. I wished Jennifer had been standing there with them.

I'm gonna miss my family. It's gonna be three long months before I can come home again. But as I watched them standing there, all together only for the hour or so it took to see me off, I also realized I'd never really be able to go home again. At least not to the family or even the house I grew up in. And I began to wonder how many other kids were leaving for college from a divided family like mine.

The first month or two of college I was almost too busy to think. But not too busy to feel lonely and wonder what Jennifer was doing eight hundred miles away. There were so many things happening, so many new experiences I longed to share with her.

In Psych 101 I did a research paper on the emotional impact of divorce on children. That got me thinking, and one day midway through the term I stopped by the counseling office to ask if there was any kind of a discussion group for kids from divorced homes. The counselor I talked to, one of the psych profs, said there wasn't but that he'd been wanting to start one if he could find enough interested people.

I did a little recruiting (Jennifer would have been proud of me) and we had seven people at our first meeting. Attendance climbed and leveled off at about twelve to fifteen people every week. The meetings were even more insightful than the ones I went to at Jennifer's high school because everyone was a little older and we tried to bring a Christian perspective into our discussion.

Some of the people have been surprised to find so many victims of divorced homes at a Christian college. And I think we're all seeing ways our parents' divorces affect us, our emotions, our personalities, our relationships, and our attitudes toward marriage. Talking about our experiences helps; and that's what keeps everyone coming back week after week.

Twice I went in for individual counseling sessions with the psych prof who helps lead the group. I summarized my story for him and told him I wanted to learn everything I could from my experience and from my parents' divorce; I wanted to make sure I could have healthy relationships and a lasting marriage. He told me it sounded like I was on the right track.

I still remember his next words. He said, "If I've learned anything from counseling kids from divorced homes, it's this: Everyone involved in a divorce is affected, whether they realize it or not. The secret to surviving as a healthy person with the potential for other healthy relationships is to recognize and understand how you are affected. Only then can you find ways to minimize those effects. If you don't admit and understand the impact divorce has had on you, you're reacting to an unknown. You're blinded to the real problems and they only get worse."

He was the one who suggested I write out my whole story as a way to better understand my experience and feelings. So that's what I've done. It's been something of a downer reliving all the rough times and remembering all the times with Jennifer. But I think it has helped. I've learned that the scars—even if they never completely disappear—do fade. And that the scars themselves are evidence of healing and new strength. They can be a reminder of what's happened and what's been learned.

The biggest thing I've learned is that God wants to make something whole and wonderful out of human brokenness. He wants me to know that I can trust him when human beings break my trust.

Knowing that, there's always hope.

Not hope for my parents' marriage. Maybe not even hope for me and Jennifer. But real hope for future relationships. And for my own marriage, when and if the time for that comes.

Other Living Books® Best-sellers

THE ANGEL OF HIS PRESENCE by Grace Livingston Hill. This book captures the romance of John Wentworth Stanley and a beautiful young woman whose influence causes John to reevaluate his well-laid plans for the future. 07-0047 $2.95.

ANSWERS by Josh McDowell and Don Stewart. In a question-and-answer format, the authors tackle sixty-five of the most-asked questions about the Bible, God, Jesus Christ, miracles, other religions, and creation. 07-0021 $3.95.

THE BEST CHRISTMAS PAGEANT EVER by Barbara Robinson. A delightfully wild and funny story about what happens to a Christmas program when the "Horrible Herdman" brothers and sisters are miscast in the roles of the biblical Christmas story characters. 07-0137 $2.50.

BUILDING YOUR SELF-IMAGE by Josh McDowell. Here are practical answers to help you overcome your fears, anxieties, and lack of self-confidence. Learn how God's higher image of who you are can take root in your heart and mind. 07-1395 $3.95.

THE CHILD WITHIN by Mari Hanes. The author shares insights she gained from God's Word during her own pregnancy. She identifies areas of stress, offers concrete data about the birth process, and points to God's sure promises that he will "gently lead those that are with young." 07-0219 $2.95.

COME BEFORE WINTER AND SHARE MY HOPE by Charles R. Swindoll. A collection of brief vignettes offering hope and the assurance that adversity and despair are temporary setbacks we can overcome! 07-0477 $5.95.

DARE TO DISCIPLINE by James Dobson. A straightforward, plainly written discussion about building and maintaining parent/child relationships based upon love, respect, authority, and ultimate loyalty to God. 07-0522 $3.50.

DAVID AND BATHSHEBA by Roberta Kells Dorr. This novel combines solid biblical and historical research with suspenseful storytelling about men and women locked in the eternal struggle for power, governed by appetites they wrestle to control. 07-0618 $4.95.

FOR MEN ONLY edited by J. Allan Petersen. This book deals with topics of concern to every man: the business world, marriage, fathering, spiritual goals, and problems of living as a Christian in a secular world. 07-0892 $3.95.

FOR WOMEN ONLY by Evelyn and J. Allan Petersen. Balanced, entertaining, diversified treatment of all the aspects of womanhood. 07-0897 $4.95.

400 WAYS TO SAY I LOVE YOU by Alice Chapin. Perhaps the flame of love has almost died in your marriage. Maybe you have a good marriage that just needs a little "spark." Here is a book especially for the woman who wants to rekindle the flame of romance in her marriage; who wants creative, practical, useful ideas to show the man in her life that she cares. 07-0919 $2.95.

Other Living Books® Best-sellers

GIVERS, TAKERS, AND OTHER KINDS OF LOVERS by Josh McDowell and Paul Lewis. This book bypasses vague generalities about love and sex and gets right to the basic questions: Whatever happened to sexual freedom? What's true love like? Do men respond differently than women? If you're looking for straight answers about God's plan for love and sexuality, this book was written for you. 07-1031 $2.95.

HINDS' FEET ON HIGH PLACES by Hannah Hurnard. A classic allegory of a journey toward faith that has sold more than a million copies! 07-1429 $3.95.

HOW TO BE HAPPY THOUGH MARRIED by Tim LaHaye. One of America's most successful marriage counselors gives practical, proven advice for marital happiness. 07-1499 $3.50.

JOHN, SON OF THUNDER by Ellen Gunderson Traylor. In this saga of adventure, romance, and discovery, travel with John—the disciple whom Jesus loved—down desert paths, through the courts of the Holy City, to the foot of the cross. Journey with him from his luxury as a privileged son of Israel to the bitter hardship of his exile on Patmos. 07-1903 $4.95.

LIFE IS TREMENDOUS! by Charlie "Tremendous" Jones. Believing that enthusiasm makes the difference, Jones shows how anyone can be happy, involved, relevant, productive, healthy, and secure in the midst of a high-pressure, commercialized society. 07-2184 $2.95.

LOOKING FOR LOVE IN ALL THE WRONG PLACES by Joe White. Using wisdom gained from many talks with young people, White steers teens in the right direction to find love and fulfillment in a personal relationship with God. 07-3825 $3.95.

LORD, COULD YOU HURRY A LITTLE? by Ruth Harms Calkin. These prayer-poems from the heart of a godly woman trace the inner workings of the heart, following the rhythms of the day and the seasons of the year with expectation and love. 07-3816 $2.95.

LORD, I KEEP RUNNING BACK TO YOU by Ruth Harms Calkin. In prayer-poems tinged with wonder, joy, humanness, and questioning, the author speaks for all of us who are groping and learning together what it means to be God's child. 07-3819 $3.50.

MORE THAN A CARPENTER by Josh McDowell. A hard-hitting book for people who are skeptical about Jesus' deity, his resurrection, and his claims on their lives. 07-4552 $2.95.

MOUNTAINS OF SPICES by Hannah Hurnard. Here is an allegory comparing the nine spices mentioned in the Song of Solomon to the nine fruits of the Spirit. A story of the glory of surrender by the author of *HINDS' FEET ON HIGH PLACES*. 07-4611 $3.95.

NOW IS YOUR TIME TO WIN by Dave Dean. In this true-life story, Dean shares how he locked into seven principles that enabled him to bounce back from failure to success. Read about successful men and women—from sports and entertainment celebrities to the ordinary people next door—and discover how you too can bounce back from failure to success! 07-4727 $2.95.

Other Living Books® Best-sellers

THE POSITIVE POWER OF JESUS CHRIST by Norman Vincent Peale. All his life the author has been leading men and women to Jesus Christ. In this book he tells of his boyhood encounters with Jesus and of his spiritual growth as he attended seminary and began his world-renowned ministry. 07-4914 $4.50.

REASONS by Josh McDowell and Don Stewart. In a convenient question-and-answer format, the authors address many of the commonly asked questions about the Bible and evolution. 07-5287 $3.95.

ROCK by Bob Larson. A well-researched and penetrating look at today's rock music and rock performers, their lyrics, and their life-styles. 07-5686 $3.50.

THE STORY FROM THE BOOK. The full sweep of *The Book*'s content in abridged, chronological form, giving the reader the "big picture" of the Bible. 07-6677 $4.95.

SUCCESS: THE GLENN BLAND METHOD by Glenn Bland. The author shows how to set goals and make plans that really work. His ingredients of success include spiritual, financial, educational, and recreational balances. 07-6689 $3.50.

TELL ME AGAIN, LORD, I FORGET by Ruth Harms Calkin. You will easily identify with the author in this collection of prayer-poems about the challenges, peaks, and quiet moments of each day. 07-6990 $3.50.

THROUGH GATES OF SPLENDOR by Elisabeth Elliot. This unforgettable story of five men who braved the Auca Indians has become one of the most famous missionary books of all times. 07-7151 $3.95.

WAY BACK IN THE HILLS by James C. Hefley. The story of Hefley's colorful childhood in the Ozarks makes reflective reading for those who like a nostalgic journey into the past. 07-7821 $4.50.

WHAT WIVES WISH THEIR HUSBANDS KNEW ABOUT WOMEN by James Dobson. The best-selling author of *DARE TO DISCIPLINE* and *THE STRONG-WILLED CHILD* brings us this vital book that speaks to the unique emotional needs and aspirations of today's woman. An immensely practical, interesting guide. 07-7896 $3.50.

The books listed are available at your bookstore. If unavailable, send check with order to cover retail price plus $1.00 per book for postage and handling to:

Tyndale DMS
Box 80
Wheaton, Illinois 60189

Prices and availability subject to change without notice. Allow 4—6 weeks for delivery.